Modjeska

BOOKS BY ANTONI GRONOWICZ

Modjeska

HER LIFE AND LOVES

BY ANTONI GRONOWICZ

NEW YORK: THOMAS YOSELOFF, INC.

Printed in the United States of America
American Book—Stratford Press, Inc., New York

TO
GRETA GARBO

AUTHOR'S NOTE

THIS BOOK is based on twenty years of research, interviews, and travel throughout Europe and America gathering material on the life of the great Shakespearean actress, Helena Modjeska. The dialogue introduced in these pages is conceived from the Polish notes of Modjeska, together with conversations held by the author with those who lived with the actress and worked with her. New and unknown facts coming to the attention of the author have enabled him to present what he sincerely hopes is a complete picture of Modjeska's life and her contribution to the art of the theatre.

CONTENTS

ILLUSTRATIONS

(The illustrations, grouped as a separate section, will be found
following page 128)

ILLUSTRATIONS

(The illustrations, grouped as a separate section, will be found following page 128)

Modjeska

1. PANTHEON OF GHOSTS

IT WAS the summer of 1908. All the blinds were kept drawn in the strangely silent house on Bay Island, California, and had been for months. Unpleasant rumors had begun to spread.

It was known that the "greatest Shakespearean actress of the age" Helena Modjeska was staying there. Still a woman of rare beauty and famous throughout the world, she could not move anywhere without becoming the center of interest and curiosity, and now she had abruptly shut herself off. All letters and telegrams were ignored. Anxious friends were frightened away by huge dogs that flew at the locked iron gates.

Now some of the most persistently curious had reported hearing the celebrated voice issuing from the house in feverish unanswered monologues. No one could make them out. Was she studying some new and tragic role? Among the list of Shakespearean characters that rolled out in rich passionate tones, the name of Igo Neufeld was heard more than once. And who was he? Madame Modjeska, the gossips said, seemed to be undergoing some terrible inner torture, or else she was acting the part out—pleading, jeering, threatening, wailing, and grieving.

It was true. In her house, deliberately cut off from the world, the great actress was playing a part. But on this occasion she was playing it for herself, and she was playing it before those ghosts of the past that had persecuted her, that had torn away something of her soul.

" . . . Perhaps you are right. It's a mere speck of an island. You won't even find it on a map. The Pacific Ocean is so huge. . . . So . . .

"But things have changed I tell you. *I* live here now. Every soul on earth knows of this island. Do you understand? . . . I am Modjeska.

"But who are *you*? You stand there like a shadow. Speak to me. Are you his mother? You have cost me so much. Ah, I don't

15

mean money! Why should I care about what I sent you to pay for your trip to this country? I have plenty of money . . .

"Did the ocean frighten you? Yes, I can understand that. But you had to be brave. A chance you had to take, wasn't it? You must win or you must lose. It's all a chance. Where would I have been if I had not taken chances? And besides, the great Pacific has its own concerns and takes its own victims. What time has it to converse with the waters of the Vistula about your son? Or to take vengeance upon you or upon me? Look for yourself. I am still here, alive. No one has touched me, not even the ocean. But wait . . . you're trying to deceive me! You didn't cross the Pacific. It was the Atlantic, and you took the train to Los Angeles. I remember I warned you by letter not to come by the Pacific. You see I remember distinctly?"

She was dressed in a light blue flowing gown. She was tall and beautifully formed. Standing at the edge of a square porch beside one of its marble columns, she was like the spirit of classicism. For a while only her lips moved, forming indulgent phrases with careful modulation. She looked out across the little path that led down to the gate. It was flanked by rose bushes. The scent of them weighed oppressively on the hot and humid air. She held her left arm above her head, her long thin fingers supporting the keel of a vase in the shape of a Greek ship. Now with a consciously graceful gesture she raised her right hand in greeting to a visitor.

The porch columns were slim and white like tusks of mammoths, as if they had been dug up from the desert sands and set out in a row, an appropriate sign of welcome to the past.

Helena Modjeska greeted the past, but hardly as a friend that would sweetly soothe her. To her the past was an unwritten drama of tragic implications, in which she was doomed to play the leading role.

"Madame Neufeld, why don't you say anything? How well you know that it was by your own silence you killed your son! And now you aim that weapon of silence at me. Oh . . . ! You are admiring my dress? Is that why you gaze at me so strangely? Do you like it? It's the gown worn by Lady Macbeth. And you know what she did, the crimes she committed. But you don't want to look into my eyes. Always at my dress. It is really noth-

ing to look at. You should have seen the costumes I designed
myself for *Henry VIII*. There was one of black plush with jet
and a profusion of real lace, and so many others! Altogether
they cost me two thousand seven hundred dollars. Think of that
—almost three thousand. You see, I am rich. But come inside.
I will show you these costumes and hundreds more. And I will
act out a few parts for you, for I don't appear in public any
more. . . . But you are so late. Why are you so late? Europe is
not so far away. You can't blame me for it. I sent you enough
money, and I gave you the address. It was quite clear. I remember as if it were yesterday—four times on the envelope and four
times in the letter: Helena Modjeska, Bay Island near Newport,
Orange County, California."

Her lips ceased to move, and her right hand fell to her side.
Her large eyes pierced the sun-broiled path for several minutes
before she spoke again. "I see you come empty-handed, when I
asked you expressly to bring me some water from our Vistula.
It was the one reason I asked you to come here, for no one else
should know the secret. In the middle of the night I thought of
it. It came to me that only you could help me. When the devil is
powerless, he sends a woman, or so they say. But, Madame Neufeld, I see you have tricked me. Is this your way of paying me
back?"

She lowered her left arm, her fingers clutching at the little
Greek ship, as her mounting rage made her tremble, and a heavy
perspiration broke through the white band around her forehead,
ran down to her strongly marked eyebrows, and streaked her
lean cheeks as if she had been weeping. Then she paused. Were
these really tears upon her cheeks? Slowly her body relaxed. She
seemed to want to make excuse for her behavior.

"When I sit alone on this porch, I look at those purple hills
of Santa Ana, or up at the peaks of Sierra Madre. Or sometimes
I look across the blue waters of the bay. Then there is peace
within me, and I am quite calm. But now your coming has upset
me."

She hesitated as if she expected an answer, and stared at the
invisible, stubborn personage, her visitor from across the ocean,
but Madame Neufeld remained silent. Helena Modjeska leaned
forward like a bird about to swoop down from the porch and

she screamed: "Come on in! Come on in!" And she broke suddenly into loud metallic laughter, turned about and ran into the
semi-darkness of the immense room beyond. She held the door
a moment before closing it firmly. She leaned against it, her face
turned to the center of the room.

"Now you understand me. You can always tell a fool by his
laughter."

She seemed to take the silence for agreement. With the air
of Lady Macbeth she began to pull the curtains over every window. No trace of daylight should penetrate into this room, no
peeping eyes from the world outside. How could one tell? Perhaps that busybody Doctor Boyd was peering through some
crack, or even her husband Count Bozenta. Or perhaps Edwin
Booth would suddenly rush in. The door must be locked. This
must be a secret between Madame Neufeld and Igo and herself.
Perhaps Aunt Theresa knew something about it, but Aunt
Theresa could always be trusted, and deep in her heart had always wanted this union between Helena and Igo, even though
her wisdom made her oppose it.

"But today she will be here to give me strength," Helena was
reassuring herself. She lit the candles on a crystal candelabrum,
which stood on a marble table. The light shone on a large vase
filled to the brim with a colorless liquid. Helena turned to face
the room, her voice triumphant. "See, I do have water from the
Vistula. I knew you would disappoint me, but I outwitted you."

Without waiting for any answer from the shadow of Madame
Neufeld, she raised a candle from its socket and dipped it toward the water. The candle suddenly flared a halo of light
around the handsome face of Helena, before it abruptly hissed
and died. She lifted her eyes to the mural on the wall above,
where a river was rolling through thickets and reeds and flowers,
with the bastions of the city behind, and on the banks a group
of boys and girls were all laughing save one boy. He sadly held
the hand of a girl in a lace dress, but she was laughing like the
others.

Helena was thinking that she had always loved many paintings on her walls. She turned now to the portrait of the famous
American actor, John McCullough, shown with gray hair, and
below him the balcony scene from *Romeo and Juliet* with his

inscription: "Helena, you are the greatest artist I have ever seen and I foretell for you unusual triumphs on our stage!" She stared into his pale face, his sad eyes. How strange that he looked so like the solemn boy by the river!

She turned away, and let her eyes linger briefly over the other paintings, scenes from *Adrienne Lecouvreur, As You Like It, Twelfth Night, Othello, Macbeth, Hamlet.* She had received an ovation in all of them, but now the strange face of the boy by the river solemnly holding the laughing girl's hand seemed to dominate each picture, his dark eyes peering at her by the ghostly light of the candles.

The gown of Lady Macbeth no longer satisfied her and she pulled it off. She dressed herself as Adrienne, parading gracefully among books, pictures, and rugs, and the various costumes strewn upon the floor. Her eyes flashed a challenge to the past glory on the walls, but the boy's sad dark eyes looked through her. Once again she cast off her gown and swiftly clothed herself in the diaphanous vesture of a still magnificent Cleopatra, but she murmured with a bitter smile: "Behold my body, look upon my raiment."

The silence of the room became oppressive. Well, there was the role of Rosalind. She picked up the costume from the floor, and began to change. There was still something of youth in her body, but her face had become pale, like alabaster, and her body began trembling. "They all loved me as Rosalind. New York, Boston, Philadelphia. James T. Fields, Oliver Wendell Holmes, Thomas Bailey Aldrich, even Longfellow wrote me beautiful letters."

Helena Modjeska became silent, as she fell to the floor, her hair cascading over her breasts. No words came to her ears in answer. Then she looked up suddenly, a light in her eyes. "Perhaps Viola?" she shouted. "When you saw me do *Twelfth Night* you told me yourself you thought I was wonderful. You spoke of my genius then." She sat rigid, staring straight ahead of her, gathering strength to look at the painting by the river. "Why don't you speak to me, Igo? You wanted me to be famous. You wanted me to be greater than any other Shakespearean actress. You told me so again and again and again. I remember so well how you said it, how I looked at you, watched you saying it. It might have been only yesterday. You talked about the 'Goddess of Art.' I have done it, Igo. What more can I do? Can't you speak? Tell me that I've pleased you. Tell me I'm the best. Tell me I'm beautiful, that I've conquered the whole world with my art."

Her impassioned words died on the still hot air, and there was no answer. She lifted her head and with tearful eyes looked upon the painting of the sad boy and smiling girl. She caught the dark burning in his look, as if he waited for a miracle to pass. She sank her eyes into his lips, his still full, sullen lips. She was waiting for an answer, a single word even. Surely he must speak. Yet silence throbbed like the heart of a great clock —fifteen minutes, thirty minutes, until Helena's head fell slowly to her breast and she sobbed deep affecting tears, in a way that only she could do.

But old and handsome John McCullough, he was moved, and stepped out from her memory into the center of the room. He gravely looked at her.

"Good John," she said, brushing her long red hair away from her tear-wet face. John, too, had cried, but from joy, when he saw her as Ophelia. Now the shadow of John bent over her in silence and caressed the waves in her hair, until she became quiet again.

On one sunny afternoon in London the crowds had unhitched the horses of her carriage and drawn it through the streets, raising hosannas in her honor. Now her eyes moved to the walls again. There were scenes there of her engagement in London at that time. Her whole body became seized with emotion. She trembled as the shreds of other events leaped to life—Paris, Vienna—where the whole family of the Emperor came to her premiere. Parties and celebrations until dawn. Then Cracow— that entire city celebrated her triumph, with masses of fluttering red and white flags and seas of flowers.

Suddenly she cried out, "Igo, do you want me to come to Cracow, now—at once?" She seemed unaware of the silence now, her face lit up as she remembered the town of her birth where their love so traitorously came to flower. Her pale thin fingers combed at her hair, until she felt she was young again, wanted, and bright with happiness. She got to her feet and moved across to the light of the candles, and it was as if she were making her way through a great crowd of people.

She began to gather the strewn costumes from the floor as she murmured, "To come back, come back?" She worked with haste, but her words expressed her doubt. "I tell you you'll be sorry. So many years have gone by. What is it now? Nineteeneight, or -six, or -seven is it? It is so late, so late. I am old now. Nothing can be done. Look at my hands, my face, my breasts. . . . Oh no, I am old! And you are so young, so young. . . . All my friends are here. Why should I go back. Even John McCullough will laugh at me, an old woman returning to love. . . . Think it over, Igo. Why not stay with me in America and not go back to the old places, to the old times. I think everything must have changed. The old places must be rotting away, bitter with age, and evil-smelling. You see, in the moonlight the Vistula looks so different, and even the sound through the reeds is a different sound. Look at the water your mother brought from the Vistula. It's not the same."

She dropped the gathered costumes on the floor and turned to the scene by the river. "Everybody's here in the room. Look down from where you are and you'll see. There in the corner is your shrewd mother. And there is my aunt Theresa with my only sister beside her. Here on the left is your father, Doctor Neufeld. He has just finished examining my mother and gently consoles her. Do you remember what your father used to say? 'Some follow blindly the leaders with elastic conscience and strong physique, others who have lost faith in life on earth spend their time looking up to heaven. Only a handful lives by the strength of heart and mind, and these will bring about the salvation of the world from the clutch of fear and hate.' These words are wise. Do you hear them? They cured my mother. Do you hear them? But look around. Everyone is here who saved himself from the Cracow fire. Is it hard to see in here? Take the candlestick then and search through the house. In every corner there will be someone you know."

She did not wait for an answer, knowing perhaps even in the disorder of her mind that there would be no answer, and she raised the candlestick from the table and moved close to the wall.

"Take the light. Come down from your heights and look around you. See for yourself. Take the light."

The girl who smiled looked so much like her, but the boy who held her hand seemed to frown under his dark mane and his lips thinned.

"Even now you don't trust me, Igo! You won't even try to understand. We could live together now among our own people, both of us rich and famous, you as a painter, I as an actress. I kept my word. I was right. I have always been right. What are you waiting for? For me to die? You can't blame me for what happened to you. I suffered too, and maybe even more than you. Look at my face, my eyes, my whole body tells the story of my longing for you, how much I've suffered. If you won't believe what I tell you, then believe what you see in me. Please, please, have pity on me and come and live with me! I implore you, with my whole love!"

The face of Helena Modjeska drew in, as if it were becoming old. She paled. Her hand began to shake, so that the light flickered across her face, now white as candle wax, as it drew near to the wall until her dried lips pressed against the boy's feet. Then she moved back a little and raised the branched candlestick high above her head, a wild desperation in her eyes, the unearthly light of madness, as she looked upon the body of her lover. She stood there motionless, in agony, as all things about her melted out of mind.

One last sober thought sank into her brain that would solve all her problems. It would be her penitence, an expiation of her sins, an absolution. She saw it in Igo's face. The only action that would satisfy him, and she breathed the words out weakly: "All right, it will be as you say. I will come back to meet you there—Cracow and the Vistula, and our youth. . . . But tell me, Igo, how shall I know that the waters of the Vistula won't drown me in revenge?"

All strength gone, she began to sink down along the wall. No muscle in her body would hold her up, until her hands and her face sank into the velvet-textured mass of costumes and lace, and her listless fingers unclasped, letting the candles lean, topple, and slide, still burning, and roll along the floor.

To the very day it was exactly fifty-five years before that a fire raged through Cracow, swallowing that entire city, the birthplace of Helena, and beloved haven of castles, churches, legends, and vengeful dragons.

Now, Helena in great haste was returning to Cracow—to the past that she had never escaped, to save from the fire's fury her first love, her Igo!

2. ORDEAL BY FIRE

Not one of the oldest inhabitants of the town could remember a summer as scorched as this one. The town records were innocent of such experience, for each day the sun stood motionless in the Cracow sky, staring down like some horrible monster with its gullet open, hissing out a constant stream of unbearable heat. The older citizens saw in the sun the dragon of legend.

Two thousand years ago—so this legend went—such a monster had lived in a cave not far from the castle of Wawel, and became the scourge of the land, devouring the property of the good knights of Cracow. The loss of their chattel slaves and their prisoners of war was disturbing enough, but the loss of their herds of cattle was too much to suffer with equanimity. When all attempts to slay the dragon in combat had failed, the valiant Krak discarded his weapons and turned to the use of his wits. He stuffed a sheepskin with sulphur and set it down at the entrance of the monster's lair. When the dragon came out, he saw the offering and devoured it whole. At once his insides became like a burning furnace. In an agony of thirst he thundered down to the banks of the Vistula. There he drank and drank and drank, in the vain hope of putting out the fire which seemed to rage inside his body. He drank so much water that at last he burst with an explosion that rocked the town. This was the monster's end, but with his last breath he vowed vengeance upon the descendants of the noble Krak.

So spoke the legend, and the people did not question the truth of it. Now, at the expiration of two millenniums, the monster's vow was being fulfilled. It was now clear to the old people that the dragon's soul had been waiting for this very time to come, meticulously selecting the exact moment for the most cruel revenge, even picking out the days as would a beggar woman at the church portal moving rosary beads: "It's a good day. . . . It's a bad day"—till the day came—this one, the last Sunday of the month of the lime trees, July of 1853.

24

In panic, the people gave themselves up to the protection of Providence, abandoning the streets that stretched out under the sun like lava beds. The more deeply pious, limp with the flood of perspiration and tears, crammed the Church of the Franciscans, the Church of the Dominicans, and the Church of the Shrine of St. John. The time-darkened steeples of the Church of the Virgin Mary creaked ominously from the strain and zeal of prayers for deliverance.

Groans and calls to God for some relief came from under the arcades of the ancient Sukiennice. The awful sounds frightened the pigeons away in flocks to stagger about the empty streets stupidly seeking water in the arid fountains. They were only saved from sudden death by the fact that the cats of Cracow had abandoned the town in search of mice in the stifling fields. The houses of the citizens stood along the vacant streets like blind and ancient men, their windows sealed, their shutters pulled firmly together. Inside, in the dark and motionless air, the people crept to the basements, while their children submerged their bodies in tubs of water, and told each other of terrible things that talked of doom.

To begin with, the iron knife which had hung in the Sukiennice ever since the building of the Church of the Virgin Mary had mysteriously vanished! That knife of a murderer! The architects of the church had been twins who worked closely together in everything they had constructed, and then shared alike as brothers should the alternate praise and scoldings of the fickle bishop. But in one of them the seed of rivalry had been planted, and during one week when his twin was absent he constructed a stronger foundation under his tower, so that when that tower climbed steadily skyward it was able to reach a more magnificent height than any tower his brother was building. Bitter with envy, the wronged man turned against his twin, setting upon him with a knife as he walked the central aisle of the new-built church. And now the tool of this horrible crime had vanished leaving only its mark like a shadow upon the wall.

The people of Cracow shook their heads with dire prophecies, and the children ran and spread the story all around the town. "It is an ill omen," said Helena Opid with large eyes to her younger sister Josephine as they soaked in tubs of water. But

Josephine had heard the news of it before and was not paying as much attention as Helena liked to get when she used her considerable talents upon a story. She fixed her black eyes upon Josephine as she spoke with a voice dripping with prediction. "There is still another thing that has happened. It is even more terrible. We are doomed, Josephine. And this is how I know. I heard the story with my very own ears from old Stanislaw Wrona, who looks after the castle. I swear by Saint Genevieve that it's the holy truth. I was in Stanislaw's house when he told us. . . ."

Josephine leaned over from her water-filled tub, full of deliberate curiosity. "And who else was there at Stanislaw's house?"

Aunt Theresa began yelling at the girls: "Don't you splash water all over the house!" She was going around like an angry bird swooping to rescue their clothes that lay all over the floor and over every chair in the room. Yet Helena was laughing loudly and paying no attention to her aunt. She pushed Josephine away with a lunge which sent a high wave of water over the side of her tub to splash on the long pleats of old Theresa's dress.

"Josephine, don't be a fraidy cat, and stop clinging to me. It's broad daylight, don't you see? And Aunt Theresa is here to protect you."

Josephine tossed her head in challenge. "Well, go ahead then and tell me what lame old Stanislaw said."

"Fairy tales!" Theresa, in her long black dress buttoned up to the neck and pinned at the collar with an old silver brooch, stood eying them with disapproval, her face gray and bony and severe.

Helena tossed her flaming braids about indignantly. "Not fairy tales at all. Stanislaw never tells tales, and he never tells lies either. Every word he said is the God-honest truth. And I have plenty of witnesses too. One of them is Igo Neufeld, and you know him. He's the smartest and the most truthful of everyone else in Cracow."

Theresa had no time to argue. The girls' dresses would have to be ironed for Sunday. With one look of scorn she marched out, leaving Helena triumphant.

"Aunt Theresa just won't believe anything she hears, and Mother certainly won't listen. But Igo believed it and Franek and Bolek and Jan and Magda and the others who heard it, they all believed it. And anyway the whole town is talking about it already."

"That's why Aunt Theresa won't believe it," put in Josephine helpfully. "Just because everybody else does."

The older sister threw her long thick braids over her shoulder, revealing an early beauty in her firm growing breasts. "Listen, Josephine, I'll tell you what he said. Deep under the mountain of Wawel, there is another castle. It's bigger and more beautiful than the one above ground, and it's called Grod. There are golden ballrooms there, and flaming torches are used to light them up. There are silver tables and crystal chairs. Every year the kings of olden Poland come there. They hold a council in the largest and most glorious of the ballrooms, and they play games and sing. In fact they make so much noise down there that several times old Stanislaw has heard them. For he's lived there for more than fifty years. And several times he's heard the neighing of horses and the clattering of armor, all coming up from the underground passages. But this year something more than that happened. Early in the morning, just as the sun was about to come up, Stanislaw saw him."

"Saw who?"

"Boleslaw the Valiant. He'd come up from the underground castle to walk through the rooms above."

Josephine kept so still in her tub that the water was quite calm. "What did he look like?"

"His armor was iron mail, Stanislaw said, with ornaments of gold and studded with precious stones. He held his sword in his hand. Old Stanislaw could even see his face quite clearly as the visor of the King's helmet was open. His face was dark and full of wrinkles, and battle-scarred. But his eyes were shining blue, and he had a long white moustache. Old Stanislaw was hiding behind a column, and when the King passed, Stanislaw saw that he was sad. Then out of the eyes of Boleslaw the Valiant two tears rolled down and dropped upon the floor. Old Stanislaw thought he must be dreaming to see such a thing. But he watched the King walk on and disappear at the turn of the

stair on his way to the courtyard. Then old Stanislaw rushed
to look at the ground where the King had stood and he put his
hand down where the tears had dropped, and do you know
what . . . ?"

Josephine did not know, but could only shake her head, too
busy listening to think of words. Helena continued in a hushed
voice. "He showed us his fingers. The tips of them were burned.
The tears had burned them."

Josephine shook all over in her excitement. "Does he still
have the burns on his fingers?"

"Of course."

"Then it must be true!"

"Of course it's true."

"I wonder what it means."

Helena climbed out of her tub. "It bodes no good." Flexing
her body, slim as a birch, she dripped all over the floor. "Stanislaw said it bodes no good when a king sheds tears that burn like
fire It means a cataclysm."

"A what?" said Josephine.

"Something terrible," her sister tossed off casually. Drops of
water clung to her like pearls. She brushed them off lightly with
a towel, and still naked strolled about as if searching for something in the room. But there was nothing casual about her movements. She was superbly conscious of her own loveliness, and
in a pensive pose considered what a prize she would be for the
first man she would give herself to.

Her body was well modeled. Her flesh had the firmness and
freshness of youth. Her legs were long, and she walked with
an assured, graceful motion, her long hair like dark gold in
braids that hugged the litheness of her buttocks. Possessed of
an inward satisfaction, she toured the room before the gilt-
framed looks of her family on the walls. In the full light of the
still unshuttered window, an early portrait of her mother glowed
with lovely tints of flesh, showing a woman of decided attrac-
tiveness. Flanking her in smaller frames were Aunt Theresa
and Aunt Emily. By the door was a portrait of another aunt in
a mountain woman's costume, while opposite were photographs
of Helena in various poses, even as a girl who dreams of theatrical fame would like to see herself, with the hope of a rich

husband to promote her to achieve that fame. Between two windows was another picture of Helena and Josephine in white dresses standing before a mountain cabin surrounded by fir trees. It carried Helena's thoughts back to the village where her father was born. She then moved over to the pink-curtained window and looked out at the street. She felt a sudden rush of perspiration break through her skin at the sight of this furnace-like, silent, and vacant exterior.

Josephine came out of her thoughts, still immersed in her tub of water, and cried out, "Helena, what I want to know is what Pan Gustav Sinnemayer will think of this story of old Stanislaw's."

At the mention of Gustav's name, Helena leaped away from the window, raising her voice in anger. "He'll think just the same way as I do."

Josephine's round face presented a knowing smile that seemed to contradict what her sister had said. Then she spoke deliberately. "He's so much older than you are. Why, the difference is almost twenty years. The fact that he's in love with you won't make any difference. He'll think as the older people do, like Mother, like Aunt Theresa."

Helena knew that Josephine was doing it on purpose, but she could not keep from showing her temper. With an abrupt movement she leaned forward and with her whole weight pushed her sister down under the water. Josephine struggled for air. The water splashed over the floor, on the rugs, on the wall, and on the family portraits. Josephine managed to climb out of the tub, but Helena was not yet done with her. They clutched at each other desperately, their hands slipping on wet skin. The next minute there was nothing but a tangle of twisting, squirming flesh, with the hair of Josephine and the golden plaits of Helena appearing and disappearing among legs and arms, sliding, circling, clutching, while out of their panting mouths came cries and shrieks of laughter. Then Helena slid down her sister's back and sat up, a little breathless, but talking seriously again as if nothing had happened between them. "I told you not to mention Sinnemayer to me. I've told you so many times."

"Why not?" came the inevitable question. "Everyone knows

that Pan Gustav wants to marry you and make a great actress out of you."

"None of your business."

"But I am your sister."

Helena straightened her spine so that her breasts stood out proudly. "It does not make any difference to me how old he is. He's got money and he knows all about artistic things and he sees that I've got a great romantic talent for the stage." She crossed her legs and fixed her braids, as she galloped to the end of her thoughts. "And he loves me and I love him. So!"

Josephine's eyes were fixed upon her sister's face. She knew there was beauty in that face. Helena's cheeks were paling, turning to a lovely transparency with the exception of the permanent rose tint on the cheekbones, which set off the radiance of her eyes as perfectly as a rainbow compliments the sky. She loved Helena, although she would tease her a great deal and more often than not was the cause for Helena's sudden fits of rage. Josephine sensed a good deal but did not fully understand her sister. It was true that Helena was developed mentally far in advance of her age, but that was not all. She was capricious beyond prediction. Then she would approach all things in an unusual way. There was some new twist in dressing, in playing games, even in cooking. When their mother would force the reluctant Helena into the kitchen, the girl would start out to cook some ordinary meal and end up with some outlandish concoction which no one but herself could eat and enjoy, except her Gustav and, of course, the ever-loyal Josephine.

All the careful instructions of her mother and of Aunt Theresa were of little use. Helena experimented with everything, and never did learn to make *pierogi* properly, that dish with meat, sauerkraut, or fruit which was so much appreciated in the Opid household. Helena's dislike of cooking was well understood by her sister, who hated the sight of a stove, but Helena's peculiar love of experimenting was beyond Josephine's comprehension. To the younger girl it was on a par with Helena's love for the moustachioed Gustav Sinnemayer at a time when there was poor Igo Neufeld, a youth of her own age, adoring her with every look.

In fact, Igo followed her like a shadow. Helena never chased him away. She would smile at him, take long walks with him into the fields, tour Wawel Castle with him. But this did not compare with her behavior with Pan Gustav. She would spend rapt evenings with Gustav in this very room, listening to his stories of Paris, London, Rome, and of places in far-off America. Josephine could not remember a single evening spent by Igo in this, their home on Szeroka Street. She could hear her sister explaining importantly to Igo that her evenings had to be given up to Sinnemayer as she was studying the German language, music, and the lives of the saints with him, before she retired for prayer and sleep. Josephine would have given much to speak to Igo about the whole matter, but she did not dare oppose the views of her entire family, her mother, her aunt, and her half-brothers, who seemed to place the correct and pedantic Pan Gustav upon a pedestal.

Josephine secretly waited and prayed in the Church of the Virgin Mary for Igo's ultimate victory, while Aunt Theresa would encourage hope by her whispered assurance, "Igo will conquer. He is young and time is on his side. He will make lots of money. Then Helena will marry him. But first of all he must have lots of money. That's the kind of a soul she has."

At one time Igo had made a sketch of Josephine, for he was an artist of considerable talent, and Josephine was glad to sit for him. He had flattered her, stressing the attractive qualities in her face. There was Josephine staring out from the canvas, round-faced like a pumpkin, but sweet and wistful, for all the world like a Polish peasant girl not yet bound to a man. She took care to hang the picture to good advantage so that Helena would be forced to notice it. This was no case of vanity on Josephine's part. She was trying her best to impress the importance of Igo upon her strangely obtuse sister. But in spite of her efforts, her prayers, and her secret plots, Helena gave no evidence of change in her attitude, and Josephine continued to carry inside her strange premonitions of tragedy in her sister's devotion to the wealthy Pan Gustav.

He distributed money with lavish gestures so gracefully executed that no offense or embarrassment could have reason for arising. Even Aunt Theresa could do little, for she depended on the Opids for her support. She would end all conversation about

Helena with the sanctimonious phrase, *Les mauvaises herbes poussent toujours,* while making a face as if she had swallowed a lemon.

Josephine stared gloomily across at her sister and thought: He will come again tonight. The heat won't keep him away. He'll come, having rested all day, with his moustache and the remainder of his hair slicked down, the same smooth jokes slipping off his tongue, the repeated bowings to each of the family, the same sweet nothings for the ear of Helena, and the family will operate like well-greased wheels to push Helena into a premature marriage with a man old enough to be her father.

"Pour in more water," said Helena, suddenly rousing from her reverie. She pointed to the two full pails standing near Josephine. The latter meekly obliged, and they both climbed back into tepid coolness up to their necks.

The room was drowning in hot, sticky moisture. Although the afternoon was rapidly sinking into the embrace of evening, it was a hot, clinging embrace. It was a new kind of penetrating, heavy breath which set the long-suffering Cracowians to choking in their hiding places. An agonizing despair was settling down upon them. The people were giving themselves up to the power of the vengeful dragon, their confused minds beginning to identify the dragon as some awful messenger of God. And this despite the fact that no one could penetrate the meaning of the mystery. It was put down to one of those oft-occurring manifestations of God's inscrutableness. Like, thought Josephine, Helena's love for Pan Gustav.

The people of Cracow had arrived at that stage of despair that is expressed in remaining still, waiting for the final judgment to strike. It did. Suddenly, like a bolt from heaven. It came with wild screams on earth, and it spread. People sprang up trembling at the sound of it.

"Fire! The city's on fire! Fire, fire, fire!" Nobody knew where it started, but suddenly the houses, churches, and streets were vomiting flames and smoke.

"Golebia Street is all in flames. . . . The Wielopolski Palace is hidden in smoke. . . . Prince Jablonowski's home is burning up. . . ."

"Grodzka Street . . . !"

"Szeroka Street . . . !"

And there it was plain for all to see, tongues of flame swinging wildly from roof to roof, from street to alley to square, like thousands upon thousands of devils in a joy ride. Half-dressed mobs of men, women, and children rushed out of burning homes. And those that were caught tried to flee with the devils at their heels. The world of Cracow was rolling in the smoke and the choking odor of charring houses, palaces, human flesh, clothing, and rags.

Half-sane shrieks in Polish, German, and Yiddish rose up from the scene that looked like a section of hell. *"Boze zmiluj sie!"* came the groans, but God appeared to be far, far away, out of reach of both pious and impious, for the devils flew about like the figures of a gruesome carnival, and leaped with fiery joy into the most ancient churches.

"Four churches are already burning!" cried a voice from the exodus of old people, women, and children, heading for safety with prayer on their lips.

The young people were throwing themselves into battle against the devils with pails of water supplied by a human chain. Later, water was brought in barrels, dragged in by the strong or by neighing, snorting, terror-stricken horses. The struggle was unequal. The scene was reminiscent of the spring of five years back, when the citizens of the town, in revolt against their Austrian oppressors, were bombarded by the guns of General Castiglione. But this horror surpassed Metternich's murderous assault, for unlike the Austrian's careful destruction, the dragon's vengeance knew no limit.

Number 7 on Szeroka Street, the three-story building that was the home of the Opids, was already burning. The devils were forcing themselves up from the ground floor. Madame Opid and Aunt Theresa, having escaped by a second-story window, were looking frantically for the children. Joseph, Simon, and Adolph were there; the two girls were missing. Terror was in the cry that went up from the household, for Helena and Josephine were last known to be on the top floor soaking in their tubs of water. Theresa tried to force her way into the house, with Madame Opid running in her wake and wringing her hands, "My God, my God!"

Pan Gustav appeared suddenly at their side. He seized the two women and pulled them back. "Let's put ourselves under God's protection," he begged. "It would only mean death to go in there." The heat was unbearable near the house, and he dragged the two frenzied women to the shade of a tree, nearer the street. "God will have mercy," he kept repeating over and over, as he held on to them, while eying with horror the burning walls, without the slightest faith in a miracle. Joseph, the oldest of the boys, had gone around to the back of the house, but returned in tears, wailing that he had called and called and received no answer.

At this moment, a dark figure emerged as if directly out of the flames. It was Igo Neufeld staggering out of the door with Josephine in his arms. Behind him came Helena, limping. Josephine was wrapped in a dress that was practically in shreds, but Pan Gustav jumped at the sight of Helena. She was completely naked. With cries of relief and joy the Opid household rushed to greet them. Pan Gustav was struggling with his coat, trying furiously to rip it off his back. Then he sprang forward and flung the coat around Helena's body. She accepted it with complete indifference, not looking at her protector at all. She seemed full of an inner rage, and after a moment turned her head in a cloud of red-gold hair and said crossly, "Igo saved us."

The procession of destitute people was heading out of town for the meadow of St. Sebastian. It was a weird column of ragged, maimed, and hysterical humans, whose total worldly goods had just gone up in smoke behind them. For this moment the social distinction had vanished. Everyone pressed selfishly forward, pushing and jostling, with the single instinctive desire to escape the raging flames. Common tragedy had finally equalized all men of Cracow. The social protocol for which the town was famous vanished. The great dragon of vengeance had served out impartial destruction. The lush dwellers of palace and mansion jostled in the frantic exodus from hovels and basements, imported Vienna and Paris lace crushed to rough and ragged cloth. The green pastures of St. Sebastian had become an unhappy salvation for both rich and poor.

Pan Gustav took Josephine from the exhausted Igo and carried her on. She was unconscious. "She should be taken to some house and not to the meadow," he said.

"To my house," put in Igo quickly. "I live in Krzemionki."

Gustav frowned and moved away. Igo turned to Madame Opid. She was becoming resigned to tragedy. She had already seen two men whom she had happily married go to their graves. She accepted sympathy and comfort as her right. Now she agreed immediately that Josephine should go to Igo's house, and Helena stopped and said aloud, "I will go too. Maybe Josephine will need a doctor, or somebody to be with her."

"Father is a doctor, you know," said Igo.

It was decided that Aunt Theresa would go with the girls to the Neufeld home and that the others would proceed to the meadow. With the help of a sheet which Theresa managed to borrow from a friend in the crowd, Igo and Theresa carried Josephine without too much difficulty, while Helena limped beside them.

"See that the doctor examines her well," cried Madame Opid as they left. "And let him look at that foot of yours, Helena."

It was Igo's suggestion that Josephine had merely fainted from fright. He was breathing more freely now that the hated Gustav had gone off, and he saw that Josephine was beginning to open her eyes. She stared and looked around in an effort to take in what was happening to her.

When Dr. Alfred Neufeld examined the girl, he found little the matter beyond a slight nervous shock and abrasions on the shoulder. She was promptly put to bed with Aunt Theresa at her side—a rosary in her hand, a prayer on her lips.

In the meantime Helena had slipped out of sight to evade an examination of her ankle. It did not hurt any longer!

The sun went down in a blaze of heat which promised nothing but another day of hell for the poor people of Cracow. The Neufeld house stood on a hill, surrounded by oaks and maples. Stretched out below, Cracow lay like a flat pie that would soon burn up, for from edge to edge it was a sea of flame. Every so often, a column of fire would rise from among the clouds of black and pearly gray smoke, sharp and graceful like Gothic steeples of a church. The darkening sky seemed to be soaking up the tragic red of the burning city, and forming a long wide stripe hanging low and oppressive like the opened jaws of the angry dragon. Now and again, an echo of far-off voices seemed to climb up the hill to die among the trees in utter silence, accentuating the terrible beauty of the scene. To the right, the hills lay in a haze. They stretched toward the southern sky and became lost in the strangely unmoved snows of the Carpathian chain. To the left, in the valley the gray-blue waters of the Vistula ran their jagged course to the north and the Baltic. All around, from palisades and high roofs of Krzemionki, seekers of sensation were watching the convulsions of their ancient town, but night came with its pity and slowly spread over the valley a darker veil.

Helena watched, and under Pan Gustav's long coat she pressed her arms against her breasts to feel in her the sense of life. Her bare feet dug into the rough surface of the bench as if they would remain in this position for an eternity, while her eyes drank in the scene before her. Her lips became moist and full with the sharpness of her emotion, and they murmured words which they alone could understand, words of humble prayer and wild exaltation. She felt herself an inextricable part of this drama going on below her, her heart beating with the pounding of the flames.

Igo approached her from behind, and, coming so suddenly upon the picture that so exalted Helena, he halted in wonder. He came a little nearer. To be near her at such a moment was like a miracle. Every sense in his body burned to hold her close to him. The beautiful tragedy of a burning town worked upon him like a fever. It seemed to him that love for this girl had been born with the birth of his own body, and that only with the cessation of his own life could he shake it off.

Below them, ancient Cracow was slowly dying on the banks of the same river where, two thousand years before, the dragon had expired with a raging thirst.

3. BAD WEEDS

At the age of seventeen, Josephine Mary Misel, destined to become the mother of a world-famous actress, had been a girl of great beauty and charm, whirling giddily in the highest circles of Vienna and Cracow, doing her utmost to eliminate all trace of her humble origin. Then she had fallen in love with Simon Benda. Her marriage to him had given her the social position and the wealth she had so coveted. From then on she turned her attention to what she thought would be a less exhausting task, that of raising a family. When her husband died, she promptly fell in love again.

Michael Opid was a man of good standing who had come down from the Carpathian Mountains to teach. He handled his affairs well in the city, was an excellent husband an an adoring father. But after the birth of his third child, he died. Helena was to remember her father as a man with "a warm, unsophisticated heart, a most vivid imagination, and a great love of music." His early death left Madame Opid with ten children to care for, but the possession of considerable real estate saved her from financial cares.

Then came the Cracow fire. Madame Opid was thrown into financial straits. All hope of a peaceful life for her later years seemed ended. The oldest of her children were able to give her some support, but her expenses were enormous. Of first importance was the health of Theresa. Theresa was Helena's great aunt. She had lived with the family as long as Helena could remember and had been an immense comfort to Madame Opid in her series of misfortunes. Now in her advanced age she was suffering constantly from what Dr. Neufeld had diagnosed as tuberculosis of the bones.

If recovery was to be sought, the good doctor advised, she should be kept under observation for a number of days. If she would agree to spend a little time at his house as his guest, where she could breathe the fresh air of the hills overlooking the city, the doctor would be happy to have her.

Theresa accepted the plan only after much thought. It was hard for her after so many years of strenuous living, a woman of stubborn will, to admit to herself that she needed any sort of prolonged observation. But at last she consented to the plan, provided Helena and Josephine should be allowed to go with her. She liked the doctor as a friend. She liked the dignified Madame Neufeld. She reasoned with herself that if someone of her own family went with her she could look upon the affair as a visit among friends. It would make her feel less like a patient, and the girls would be excellent company.

As for Madame Opid, she was only too glad to be rid of Helena at this difficult time. The girl was far too obstreperous and indeed the most troublesome member of her entire family.

And yet in all these calculations, no one had considered the presence of Igo. It had been understood that he would be away on a painting trip with a friend. At the last moment the trip had been postponed, so that he was at the Neufeld house to greet the guests as they arrived. Theresa's face clouded, but she remained silent. Igo, himself, did not offer any explanation. Helena did not ask him. He wished that she would. But she chose to adopt a strange reserve toward Igo during her stay, a reserve that pleased Theresa, but puzzled and disturbed Igo. He followed her about like a quiet and nervous hound, and appeared to be making no impression. Helena was polite, even charming, but apparently indifferent.

Toward the end of the week, they went into the garden together to sit under the great oak that was the doctor's most cherished possession among his trees. The night was already crowding the scene, and somewhere in front of them a full moon was struggling with a mass of clouds. After a long silence, Igo moved a little closer.

"I don't see how I can live without you, Helena." His voice sounded strange out in the open. It did not present at all the deep feelings of his heart and blood. Half the moon began coming out, and he saw the wild leaping strength in her eyes as she looked over the valley. He spoke hurriedly as if at any moment she would take wings and follow her destiny.

"You needn't think I'd be against your theatrical career. Oh no, I'd never be like that! In fact, I've even thought out a plan for us. Listen to me, Helcia. I'll give up my painting. I'll go to medical school in Berlin, or Vienna perhaps. This way I'll be choosing a profession that will let us live well. My parents will certainly approve of that and Father will be only too glad to see me following his profession, and he'll pay for my schooling without question. You will see. Then when I get enough money for the two of us, you'll be able to study with teachers much better than Sinnemayer . . . and younger, too."

The sarcastic note which he could not hold back in the last breath seemed to move Helena to response more swiftly than any of his significant utterances. She threw back sharply, "We will all be old some day."

Igo felt unhappy. Words drained from him. The wind came up the hill and set up a laughter in the branches of the old oak that disturbed the birds in their sleep. The moon slipped its cold light into the narrow space that separated the two young people. Quietness settled down again. There seemed nothing to say. From the jasmine bushes behind them came a sweet outburst of song, and they both listened in rapture.

"That must be the father nightingale singing to his young ones," whispered Helena. Igo noted that she completely ignored his proposals. He admitted to himself that he had used the wrong approach, and that any disparagement of Sinnemayer only served to make her more stubborn about him.

Now he moved close to her, and said with the air of an expert, "Oh, no, he sings to his beloved." He put an arm around her and gently pressed her close to him for a moment. She pretended not to notice it, and confounded his deductions by leaping back to her former statement. Her flat unemotional tone chilled his heart.

"This plan of yours is very interesting, Igo. But you see, my mother wouldn't give her consent. She'd say I am too young to go away with one as inexperienced as you are. And besides, my mother's a very religious person."

"Oh, so it's because I'm a Jew!" he cut in bitterly. "Even though Sinnemayer, in spite of being a Protestant, looks more Jewish than I do."

"That doesn't bother Mother at all." Helena looked up at the cold face of the moon. "The important thing is that I have no feeling for you but thankfulness and pity."

Igo's arm slipped from Helena's hip, and the heavy silence fell like a stone between them. The oak became still again. Heedless, the nightingale passed on from melody to melody like a master musician without a soul.

Igo understood now. Now he knew what the Opids discussed among themselves when they talked of him. He understood the real reason why he was never invited to their house in the evenings as Sinnemayer was. Many pictures out of the past flashed through his mind and all these pictures were labeled with one word—*Jew*. This inscription made filthy every beautiful moment, poisoning truth and happiness. Such a situation existed despite the high reputation his father had made as a physician among the people of Krzemionki, and indeed of the whole of Cracow. Ailing people came to him on foot or riding in their carriages from all over the land to find cure. The fact that he was a Jew was of no importance to them. And when Josephine was put into the hands of Dr. Neufeld no one of the Opid household thought of raising an objection.

The Neufelds had lived there for hundreds of years. An ancestor of Igo's mother, Jacob Samson by name, was even at the court of Casimir the Great, as His Majesty's doctor and financial adviser. Another ancestor on his father's side, Lemel Hirsh, was a member of the Jewish regiment in the Kosciuszko insurrection of 1794 against the Czarist invaders. Igo even knew a poem by Lemel which began:

> The hour of glory has struck!
> Arise, brave countrymen,
> And tear down the bloody
> Banner of tyranny . . . !

Lemel Hirsh was among the five thousand Jews who gave their lives for their country, and whose deeds of bravery were set down and remembered in song and story. Igo's bitterness led him on to remembering how much Jewish blood had been spilled in 1831 when Poland again struggled against the Russians and the Germans. It had been the same sad history when the Austrian Emperor turned his guns on Cracow.

All this Jewish blood fell upon the ground of Poland, was soaked up and disappeared, but the hearts of the Christian people would not give up their prejudice. Igo, thinking of all the suffering and degradation that his people had experienced through the centuries, was wrenched to tears. It had no effect upon his love for Helena. He did not blame her for the thoughtless expression of a viewpoint held by her mother and Sinnemayer. But he could not understand how anyone could sincerely justify hatred of a people in the eyes of God. He recalled how his father would explain these things in the most simple terms, presenting the idea that the split between people had been fostered by those who could make use of disunity among nations to benefit themselves. His father would finish with a wise nod of his head. "Some day men will understand and will eradicate from their minds all racial bias and group hatreds."

"Some day. . . ." Igo muttered to himself. "But what about now?" He turned to Helena, who sat deep in her own thoughts as she leaned back against the tree trunk. "We must go back to the house," he said. "Supper must be ready by now. They'll be waiting for us."

Helena made no move. "Let's stay a little longer, Igo. The nightingale is so like magic. And I can smell the jasmine in the air."

"I must ask you, Helcia, to please forget our conversation here." His voice sounded oddly mature, in contrast to his former uncertainty. "I won't annoy you any more with my feelings for you. Please consider nothing has been said."

Helena found his chilled hand and pressed his fingers as if answering his plea. The blessing of rest was descending from the sky upon the trees and bushes, upon the flowers, and upon the dried leaves of the year before. But peace was far from Igo's heart. He found no comfort in Helena's gesture. This, he felt, was part of her pity toward him. Igo had lost all hope of arousing a deeper emotion in her. While staying at the Neufeld home, she had been courteous with everyone. She had helped Madame Neufeld in the kitchen many times and made herself generally charming, but all that time she had remained casual toward Igo. She appeared only to be waiting for the time she could leave the Neufeld home and join her family again.

And she would go back into the clutches of Sinnemayer's web! It *was* a web his rival was weaving, thought Igo, for to capture the daughter the man was elaborately courting the mother. During these weeks of Helena's stay, Igo had wanted so much to speak of this to Helena. He would have compared Sinnemayer's behavior to that of Emperor Francis Joseph who, being in love with his Austro-Hungarian realm, seething with its discontented people, played one against another with promises and illusions of favor. Perhaps Sinnemayer had the more complicated task, for his subjects were a mother and daughter, with all the complexities of a close and subtle relationship. But Sinnemayer brought to play more shrewdness than did his omnipotent Emperor.

On the other hand, Igo could not believe that Helena was really blind to what was happening to her, for the girl was certainly not seduced by romantic dreams. On the contrary, she always spoke of her future in matter-of-fact, calculating terms, and spoke of the love that she insisted existed between herself and Pan Gustav as if that were incidental to the whole plan.

"What are you thinking about?" Helena asked suddenly, as if she had guessed his thoughts.

"You're a strange girl," he said, getting to his feet.

"You want to go back, at once?" She seemed surprised.

His answer was efficient and abrupt. "Yes. You might catch cold out here. Then I would be responsible." He helped her to her feet. "The dining room is all lit up. Your aunt and my parents are probably talking about us, wondering if they should let us stay out here in the dark together."

Helena spoke with a smile in her voice. "Aunt Theresa trusts me completely. And your parents have good cause to trust you."

As they went up the slow incline to the house, the moon stepped into a mass of clouds and was lost like a hunter in the pathless forests of Kampinowska. Igo took Helena's hand and led her through the maze of trees and bushes of the Neufeld estate until they found the path leading up to the front door.

"It'll look better if you go in first," he said.

"Why?"

"Listen to me. It'll be better . . . better. . . ."

Helena suddenly kissed him on the cheek and dashed off like a frightened bird. Igo found himself alone.

As Igo entered the dining room the clock struck eleven. The table was laid with stuffed fish and loaves of white bread. There were soup plates and tea cups waiting to be filled. Helena was sitting primly at the table, waiting.

"Looks as if everyone has gone off to bed," said Igo. "But wait there and I'll heat up some soup in the kitchen."

"I'll help you." Helena jumped up and followed him to the kitchen.

The old servant Yaga had fallen asleep as she waited for the doctor's son and his guest. But she heard their footsteps approaching and quickly busied herself with warming their food. When Igo saw how things were going he caught the old woman's eye and smiled, for Yaga was looking at him with an understanding expression in her old face that made Igo pull Helena back into the dining room without a word spoken.

Igo suddenly felt happy, although his own ancestors on the walls looked down upon him from behind their long beards with a stern eye. All of them raised in the severe discipline of the Talmud, they had no way of understanding this peculiar fruit of the family tree. Igo preferred not to notice them and turned to Helena who was for some reason in a state of great exhilaration.

"Today is Friday, Igo. Why aren't the candles lit?"

"Father doesn't have them lit very often. He says it's not much benefit to anybody. Instead of burning candles he gives money every Friday to the Jewish Welfare Fund to help buy food and clothing for the poor of the ghetto."

There was an expression of astonishment on Helena's face. Igo smiled a little as he looked at her.

"I know what you'd like to ask. What kind of a Jew is my father anyway?"

Helena sat down in a chair with a high carved back and looked somewhat embarrassed. "Yes. He does seem to be different."

"The people all call him 'the learned one.' They know that he isn't strict in his religion. His faith is in humanity itself."

The puzzled look on Helena's face was still there as she mur-

mured, "Every Friday evening my mother lights a candle before the Virgin Mary in the drawing room."

"I know," said Igo. "My mother is as strict in her faith as
yours is. She was very angry at my father at first. But she has
grown used to his ways. She had to." He paused and looked at
her closely, resting one hand on the table, his dark, eager face
thrust forward. "You've been to this house on Fridays before,
Helcia, and you never spoke of the candles then."

She made a casual gesture with her hand. "Oh, I just didn't
think of them before." But she shifted her position in the chair.
It was clear to Igo that the unburned candles were making a
deep impression on her. Perhaps she was beginning to see things
in the Neufeld household in an altered light. But she didn't say
anything further on the subject as Yaga appeared with a steam-
ing bowl of soup.

"Onion soup!" Helena jumped up, clapping her hands like a
child.

Yaga grinned broadly. "Yes, Jasnie Panienko, and as tasty as
any put on the table of Prince Radziwill."

Igo laughed. "Niania Yaga loves onions, no matter how she
fixes them. But some time ago when I painted some beautiful
golden onions she said they were as ugly as sin."

"Paniczu, with your kind permission, that was quite another
thing. For how can you eat an onion on canvas?"

Helena burst into laughter as Igo made a face. But Yaga
deftly served up the soup and speed like a rolling barrel back to
her kitchen.

"Don't you think," said Igo as Helena started on her soup,
"that it's a little strange that Yaga, who brought me up from
childhood, should have forgotten to give me a sense of humor
like her own?"

"You're too much like your father, Igo."

"But I'm an artist."

"Still I don't see, Igo. How can one paint a joking onion?"

Igo frowned a little. "You see, you can say funny things too,
and you never got that from your family."

"There are many things I didn't get from my family," she
said and laughed coquettishly.

Igo looked at her solemnly as he ate his soup. Then he spoke with a peculiar kind of breathlessness. "That's true, Helena. When I look at you, you seem to be as unlike the rest of the family as could be. Of course, I'm not speaking of your acting in school plays or your recitations of Adam Mickiewicz, Pierre Corneille, Gotthold Lessing, or the fragments from the *Nibelungenlied.* . . ." As he rolled off the list he watched to see if Helena was impressed, but she was merely listening very gravely. "I'm not talking of those things. Your genius for the stage is unquestionable and it will be recognized without any help from others. But what is so remarkable and so mystifying in you, Helena, is your behavior as a girl in relation to your environment, to your family, to your closest friends, to . . . ."

"Stop!" She had jumped up. "Don't go on! I know very well what you're going to say!"

The next minute she had run around the table and across the dining room, so that Igo could hear her quick steps down the corridor and into the garden. Igo felt bewildered, but he sprang up instinctively and followed her as she flew straight toward the arbor at the end of the path where the jasmine grew in a grove of birches.

The moon poked its head out of a collar of feathery clouds and stared after the running girl, brightening the wind-caught waves of her copper-red hair, the angry rush of her blue dress, and her dark, furious eyes. The abrupt strengthening of the moon seemed to indicate the need of new treatment for Helena. A direct and forceful approach, untouched by sentimentality might have subdued her willfulness. But would Igo know enough to supply what was needed?

Helena reached the brush-hidden arbor, dropped on the old bench, and broke into sobs. In a second Igo was beside her, kneeling at her feet and caressing her knees with trembling hands, kissing the hem of her dress and begging forgiveness. The moon was circling the arbor as if to get a better view of the interior, but was having trouble getting past the dense brush. Helena slid to the ground beside Igo. He took courage and put his arms about her. His burning lips found her mouth, and she clung to him urgently, until the silent arbor seemed to whirl around them.

At this moment, Helena's premeditated cunning and Igo's diffidence took flight before the unity of desire. Their fingers clutched wildly to prevent even a second's disruption of their fierce-flowing happiness.

Suddenly, as if from under the ground, came a barking, hysterical voice: "What kind of a crime are you committing?"

Their arms unlocked and they jumped to their feet. Aunt Theresa, with her closed hand like a fist, was standing before them. Lit by the moon and in her nightgown, she looked more than anything like the disheveled Teutonic devil, Kusy. She grabbed Helena's unbraided hair and dragged her away, yelling at the top of her voice a flood of incoherent words.

About noon of the next day, Krzemionki had a distinguished visitor. Pan Sinnemayer, dressed in his Sunday best, with a high collar smelling of sweaty rubber and a black cape hanging over his left shoulder, made his way up the hill to the house of the Neufelds. A short distance before the gate, he began swinging his black cane with its silver handle in a decidedly menacing manner. He tipped his high black hat slightly to give a more ferocious appearance, and screwed his face into the most severe expression his yellowish overfed face could muster.

Pan Gustav had orders from Madame Opid to fetch the girls away immediately. Aunt Theresa had left for Cracow before dawn to relate the awful consequence of proximity with Igo. After a family consultation, Sinnemayer was delegated the task. It happened that the doctor was not home. There was only his wife who had already been told by her son what had happened the night before.

Sinnemayer entered through the kitchen, where Yaga was trudging about singing her peasant songs.

"Is the Doctor in?"

"Is Pan Wielmozny a patient? If so, he should be entering by the front door."

"I am not a patient," yelled Sinnemayer. "I have a private matter to settle."

Yaga's mumbling came to a stop, and she opened a pair of wide eyes at the strange gentleman with the moustache and fierce countenance.

He yelled again, "The Jews have raped the girl!"

Yaga's mouth opened as wide as her eyes, then she repeated

his words like an incompleted echo: "The girl . . . Jews . . . !"

Madame Neufeld and Helena appeared at the door.

"Dobrodziej wants to see who?" Yaga queried, but Sinnemayer pushed past the huge form and strode up to Helena, yelling in her face and hitting the floor with his cane. "The Jews have raped you! The Jews have raped you!"

Yaga approached him from the side, and grabbing his arm that held the cane, yelled louder than he: "Shut up! Nobody raped nobody!"

Sinnemayer was disconcerted. It appeared that he did not know what to do next. What made matters worse for him was the loss of his cane. Yaga's violent jerking had cast it into a cluster of empty pails in the corner. At this moment, Josephine appeared and added insult to injury by ridicule. "Pan Gustav, I watched you from the top of the pear tree as you came up the hill. And you breathed heavily like a blackmith's bellows. It could be heard a mile away!"

Madame Neufeld smiled slightly, and so did the others. The doctor's wife spoke with a great quietness. "Won't you please calm yourself? I am Dr. Neufeld's wife. You must realize that no Jews have raped any girl in this house."

"No? And Helena?"

"No," replied Helena curtly. "No one's done any harm to me, and I must ask you to please behave as a gentleman should."

Gustav's face turned pale. He took off his hat and picked up his cane. "Helena, Josephine, let us go from here at once. Your mother has requested that you leave immediately and return to her."

Madame Neufeld turned without a word and disappeared behind the heavy pine doors. The girls followed her in silence. Gustav was left stranded in the middle of the kitchen, his arms loaded with his cane, his hat, and his heavy black cloak. Beads of perspiration formed on his forehead and ran down to his moustache. Yaga shoved a stool in his direction. "Sit down, Wielmozny Dobrodziej, and take this towel to wipe your sweat."

Gustav obeyed her like a scolded boy, and after a long hesitation, asked quietly, "Are they getting ready?"

"God knows! Probably," stated Yaga, picking up her peasant song where she had left it.

"Out of my soul a sigh goes forth
Of silent longing, into the distant haze.
'Tis a memory in my heart
O years gone by, my childhood days.

Flies my song straight from the soul
To find my home along the village ways.
The thought is with me like a distant star.
'Tis years gone by, my childhood days."

No more than half an hour had elapsed when Helena and
Josephine reappeared in the kitchen, dressed to leave. Gustav
sprang to his feet and led the way out of the house without a
word. Some ten steps behind him marched the girls. They passed
the gate in this manner, in silent single file, and soon found
themselves on the dusty road which ran from the heights of
Krzemionki down to Cracow.

Through the exhilarating air, saturated with the sweet odors
of clover and camomile, bees, ponderous with pollen, passed
them. In the fields on both sides of the road all the way to the
town, peasants wearing white smocks encircled with red straps
were busy harvesting the crops. The ringing of sickles and
scythes became loud as the well-ripened rye came down to be
bound in sheafs. These in turn were piled together and, from a
distance, gave the impression of diminutive peasant huts.

Other reapers were gathering the wheat and the barley—their
shoulders bent, their linen shirts wet with perspiration as they
advanced in steady, endless motion. Overseers on spirited horses
were galloping up and down the fields with long whips in their
hands. The whistling of the whips through the air had become
a symbol of the great glory of the nobility, their wealth already
indicated in the huge mounds of sheafs waiting to be carted to
the barns. There would be no rest for the sullen peasant folk
until after the winnowing of the grain with hand flails, for only
then would the golden grain flow to the markets to bring the
golden talars into the purses of the lords.

The two girls, following behind the impatient Gustav, kept
their eyes on the fields. They took no notice of where they were
going, of the city burned to the ground with only fragments of
black walls and chimneys still standing, and an occasional church

spire towering impossibly high in the midst of its charred and flattened surroundings. Joy was absent. Oppression held them bound. God's heavens spread out free above them, but town and fields knew no escape from bondage. The overworked peasants were ruled by the overseer's whips. The overseers were themselves watched closely by the lords' land stewards.

Helena suddenly turned her face away from the fields and spoke for the first time in her life with deep resignation. "Remember, Josephine, how Aunt Theresa is always saying—'*Les mauvaises herbes poussent toujours*'? Well, it fits the Polish way of life perfectly. Perhaps the whole world is like this too."

Josephine looked at her sister solemnly but did not answer. In silence they approached the gates of the old city.

4.   THE NIGHT OF ST. JOHN

IT HAD long been the observation of Aunt Theresa that Helena was somewhat too much like her mother had been before her first marriage. Madame Opid had been impressed by this and attempted in every way she could to eradicate from her daughter's character all evidence of her own instability, but without visible success. Her despair made her reason in the following manner: Helena must marry a man of means, but one not too young. There must be no question of many children. She should be allowed to develop her own theatrical career even while she is governed by a strong hand. The conclusion for Madame Opid was self-evident. Instead of being sent to a private school, Helena must complete her education at the Convent of the Sisters of St. John. There, under stern care, living for a time a modest, ascetic life, Helena should learn obedience and become a good wife for Pan Gustav Sinnemayer.

The plan was discussed in detail with Pan Gustav, who was contributing increasingly to the support of his future wife's family. He was very much pleased with the idea, for he knew well that the Holy Sisters never permitted a Jewish boy to visit the convent, and that the girls were strictly prevented from leaving the place at any time unattended.

Madame Opid anticipated considerable opposition from her daughter and took care to impress upon her that if she refused to go to the convent her mother would have nothing more to do with her. But Helena was deeply concerned with hastening the completion of her studies as the major step toward her stage career. With but little protest, she walked solemnly through the gates of the old convent, and for a time was lost to the world. She studied languages, mathematics, Greek and Roman history, music, and diction under the vigilant eye of the sisters. The winter passed in dreary routine, until with the coming of summer the girls were permitted to take occasional walks with the sisters to the Rocks of the Virgin or to Bielany.

Helena was naturally quite religious. She prayed several times a day to the most Holy Virgin and read the lives of the saints with fervor, but the months of close confinement had made her increasingly restless. She began to prepare an escape. Her family would no doubt disown her. She would be left without a penny, but she reasoned that it would merely mean that she would continue her studies under different conditions, for she would make a living by joining the provincial theatre. In her mind this would be a simple enough matter. Even at the age of fifteen or sixteen she had shown her capabilities on the amateur stage by appearing with remarkable success in the *White Camellia* and *Primadonna—Half-Sister,* produced in Cracow, in Bochnia, and in Wieliczka.

The approach of Sobotka gave Helena the inspiration for flight. Sobotka was a custom older than Cracow itself. It took place most frequently on a Saturday, on the eve of the holidays of St. John the Baptist or on Whitsuntide, and was celebrated with the floating of wreaths on the waters of the Vistula, and the lighting of bonfires on the river's banks. The custom dated back to pagan days when it was a part of a ritual to honor the sun, as lord of all creatures who served life and death according to his whim. It had become such an established tradition among the people that in the fourteenth century, after four hundred years of Catholicism in Poland, the Bishop of Poznan had issued an edict which prohibited the celebration of this festival. The edict was ignored. Two hundred years later the Chronicler Marcin from Urzedowo wrote: "On the Eve of St. John our women are burning fires, dancing, and singing in honor and prayer to the sun devil. They still hold on to this custom of pagan times, making sacrifice of wormwood and mugworth and various other flowering species. They are adorning their heads with wreaths, suspending garlands from their houses, entwining them around bodies in celebration of Sobotka. They build fires by rubbing twigs together to make devil's holiday song and incense."

Helena knew all about Sobotka, for it still remained an annual celebration and she herself had always taken part in it. The wreaths which the girls wore on their heads were symbols of virginity. They were dropped into the rivers so that boys could

fish them out, and each could claim the girl whose wreath he rescued. Then new wreaths would be made from the flowers of the
field, as fresh and sweet as the eager young lips of the maidens
claimed. During the ceremony of the floating wreaths, the girls
would encourage the boys with songs in chorus. The oldest of
them ran:

> A linden in the green fields
> Sadly drops its leaves.
> Beneath a tree a maiden sits
> Weaving garland wreaths. . . .

> "Why dost thou cry my maiden dear?
> What dire misfortune finds thee here?"

The song told how the maiden had lost her flower garlands in
the swift-running river. Her lover sent out two white swans to
fetch them back, but the swans failed in their mission.

> "My swans have lost thy garland wreaths,
> Nothing can I see.
> O dear and lovely maiden mine,
> I'd bring joy to thee. . . .

> "My swans have brought a piece of lace,
> Put it in my care.
> Enough to make a bridal cap
> For thy golden hair."

Helena had heard many stories of the past, telling of troubles
caused by these garlands of virginity. There was the one most
famous of Dabrowka, the Czech girl who married the first un-
crowned king of Poland, Mieszko. She spoke little Polish and
knew nothing of Polish customs, and therefore had no way of
knowing the gossip she started in court when she wove a gar-
land for her hair, until the entourage of Mieszko and his vassal
princes chided Dabrowka publicly and forced her husband to
take the wreath off her head, cut her hair short, and place a cap
on her head to signify that she was married and had given herself freely to her husband.

But as time passed, the Sobotka and the floating garlands lost
their import and became nothing but innocent folk festivals at

which the youth of all classes came to disport themselves by the banks of Poland's rivers. And if with the coming of spring the settlements along the riverside revealed a sudden growth in their population, there was little thought of that. According to the popular belief these children would be more beautiful, intelligent, and healthy than those born in wedlock, and many wealthy families would gladly take them in to rear them as their own.

On the night before the great celebration, Helena sat in her convent cell, fighting against sleep as she trimmed her long blue dress with red and white ribbons. The place was silent. All were asleep. The only witnesses to her deed were the mute images of Saints Veronica, Mathilda and Genevieve; and the Virgin Mary. Helena had wanted to write a letter of farewell to Sister Superior Regina, but there was no time for that. She felt it more important that her dress look distinctive. "God will forgive me," she thought to herself, "and if He should forgive, then Sister Regina will do so too."

Looking upon the image of the Virgin Mary smiling sweetly down at her, she whispered: "You know well that the convent is no life for me. But that I must go and live free and become a great actress." The very blue eyes of the Mother of God continued to look with sweetness and kindness into the black eyes of the girl. This was important, for out of these eyes came a strange peace that filled Helena's heart.

Not many hours passed before the candle in the clay niche ornamented with painted flowers began to flicker as if exhausted. Helena grew heavy with fatigue, the silence pressing down upon her shoulders and her copper-red head. Bit by bit, the images of the holy virgins were losing themselves in the darkening gray of the walls. The candle blinked as if desperately calling for help against the forces of darkness. But as no help came, the flame staggered and died, entombed in the flower-painted niche. All the city slept. Only the trumpeter from the steeple of the Church of St. Mary broke the silence every hour, guarding the people according to a custom as old as the Tartar invasions.

The following day was the twenty-third of June, the memorable Eve of St. John. For a week now, the dealers in men's and women's clothing, the merchants of candles, drinks, and flowers were busy preparing themselves for the occasion. The streets this day were alive with the bright display of fashion. Silk parasols of most lovely ladies floated gracefully over the heads of the crowds like the Chinese gold and silver pagodas displayed in Cracow's panopticon of the world's wonders.

On the cleanly swept sidewalks of what was known as Line A and B, shooting out of the market place where the ancient Sukiennice stood, the two eccentric Mycielski twins made a studied and graceful entrance, as they had been doing for decades. In this most exclusive quarter of the town they paraded side by side, looking exactly alike with their toupees glistening, their tight-fitting coats and skintight pants of gray, their necks sprouting from high and hard winged collars supporting sideburns à la Byron, and tipping their hats constantly to the ladies of society with a smile on each face and a courteous greeting intoned in unison.

Equally impressive in its monotonous routine, but touched with buffoonery, was the appearance of two middle-aged sisters of aristocratic bearing, fair hairdo and corpulent figure made more impressive by the immensity of their hooped skirts. They took possession of the entire sidewalk as they moved up and down the same street and market place with a perpetual smile upon their lips for two hours each day at high noon. At one-thirty by the clock, as if by command, the town fool Pawelek would appear at their side, and would busy himself around their wide hoops trying to find a way to reach their lips with a kiss. A riot would always occur to the delight of the onlookers. The sisters would withdraw, leaving the embrace-hungry Pawelek desperately trying to steal a kiss from any female at hand. Invariably the show would end with the appearance of a policeman, who would lead Pawelek away. Such a performance would be repeated each day from early spring until late fall. It was as much part of Cracow life as the Cardinals in the Vatican.

But on the eve of St. John's everyone, without exception, dressed himself in his finest clothes. The ancient pagan tradition would hold complete sway. The churches could do nothing but retreat into disapproving silence. Behind the walls of the Convent of the Sisters of St. John supper was served at the unusually early hour of five, which was calculated to give the nuns sufficient time to count the girls and herd them into their cells for the night. The heathen noises from the streets would have little chance of entering here, and a double guard would be set over the cells for most of the night.

As soon as the count was over, Helena with a most innocent sweetness approached Sister Hedwig. She wanted to gather some flowers in the garden, she said, to place them before the Virgin Mary. The sister was touched and agreed. Helena went quietly into the garden, her festive dress concealed beneath her long cloak. She began to gather flowers, and moved slowly toward the garden wall. It seemed higher than ever now, its top menacing with its embedded glass and china fragments. She sat down on the bench beneath the lilac bush to think the problem out. Her eyes fell upon the thick trunk of a linden which grew so near to the wall that its huge branches spread out far over the top. With one jump she dropped into the high grass at the base of the tree and crouched like a hare with beating heart to wait for total darkness.

With the coming of night the crowds streaming toward the river could be heard beyond the wall, and Helena's heart was strengthened. She pulled herself up to the first low branch and, catlike, clawed her way on until she could look down over the wall. Then she threw her cape across the glass pieces and slid gingerly down on top of it. Gathering strength, she took hold of the end of the cape and let herself drop to the wooden sidewalk. She had done it without a scratch. No one seemed to pay much attention to her, and she quickly lost herself in the crowd.

She first headed for the meadows to get wild flowers for her wreath. The voices of the crowd faded behind her, together with the remembrance of the deep warning of the Sister Superior: "Be good, be good, be good!" All past things were becoming drowned in the exciting scent of flowers and dewy grass. Helena found herself singing over and over, "Now I'm free, now I'm free!" It would mean a new life. Fires were already catching along the river banks, as Helena approached. She ran from one to the other in the hope of finding a friend. At the fourth she came upon Lucy Studzinski, a pupil of Madame Hoffman at the Dramatic School, but the girl looked somewhat solemn for such an occasion.

"Why so pensive?" Helena said.

Lucy leaped to her feet as though she had seen a ghost. "But you're in the Convent, aren't you? They couldn't have let you out just for St. John's night?"

"Of course," Helena laughed. "Otherwise I wouldn't be here." She sat down at the crackling fire. "But you still didn't answer my question, Lucy."

"Oh well, my Jasiek is sick. Most likely he won't be able to come tonight."

Helena chanted recklessly, "What of that? What of that? Someone else will fish out your wreath."

A boat was floating slowly along the water's edge. Suddenly Helena heard a voice ringing in wild excitement: "Helcia! H-e-l-c-i-a!" Helena turned around.

Igo was shouting for joy. "I looked all over for you!"

She ran down to the sandy part of the bank. He had beached the boat and was striding toward her, but he stopped. Helena had stopped too. Their eyes met. It was all that was needed.

Igo had not forgotten that Helena had told him in the wintertime that she would meet him at the Sobotka no matter how difficult it would be. They were walking together now in the current of excited young people who were searching for the best place to throw wreaths. The boats were half in the water in readiness. Huge bonfires lit up the night, and songs flew up into the air like flames on every side. As soon as the girls were ready, the boys would rush for their boats. With the words of the old song in their ears, "The swans are swimming . . . the garlands are sinking . . ." they would shoot out into the current after the wreaths of their choice.

Helena pulled Igo away into the thicket of high reeds with her wreath still in her hair. The farther they moved away from the noise of the river and away from the monster fires, the faster walked, locked in close embrace. The high reeds, the tall grass and brushwood swallowed them up. They pushed madly on until they fell to the ground beneath a small willow, clutching at each other as if nothing could ever separate them again.

The willow leaves, the million reeds, the sounds from the river, spun about them and merged into a single entity—the odor, the sensation, and color of two bodies joined as one. Saturated with song, the night with rhythmic motion cradled them in their bed of soft and secret grasses.

Rising up with the flames on the river banks, new melodies swelled lustily to the stars and slid out onto the fields and over the city of Cracow, where the more sedate inhabitants were preparing for slumber. But the youth of the region were trapped by the Vistula and thought nothing of sleep, and nothing but dawn could release them. Until the coming of dawn there would be many hours of surprise; and for love a whole eternity.

5. THE DEATH OF THERESA

FROM HER father, Michael Opid, Helena had inherited that peculiarly mettlesome blood of the Polish mountaineer. Michael's life had been cut short in its prime, but while he lived he had bluntly stated his own philosophy: "I thumb my nose at all the world." His daughter did not use these words, but she adhered to the formula with spirit. She moved brightly from one gay moment to the next, full of the most preposterous practical jokes, and never content to leave things as she found them. Life must be bent to her own purposes. The tried and proven ways of others she detested, and when she was criticized for her outlandish behavior or openly opposed, she seemed always able to turn the tables with engaging laughter or with some new and crazy trick.

The displeasure of others bothered her little, it was true, for some destiny drove her on regardless. She must be herself, not what others wanted her to be. This self-assurance and openhearted, if disconcerting, sincerity attracted to her those of open mind and higher wisdom—very few among the narrow-minded, gossipmongers of Cracow. Even her own mother, who had closed out all remembrance of her young years with Michael, felt quite helpless before the willfulness of her daughter. The only one who could hope to understand her was her half-brother Simon Benda, but he was studying in Vienna. As for her only sister, Helena was ready to share a great deal with her. But Josephine, knowing full well that her mother was busy concocting a suitable marriage for her, was making the most of her last days of freedom.

There was no one else in the family to talk to. Not great Aunt Theresa. That shrewd-looking, gray-haired, black-laced woman was now slowly dying, though no one was allowed to mention it, pretending to conceal it from her, and she in kind pretended not to know. The fact was old Theresa knew everything. Helena was aware of that, and it made her uneasy. Aunt Theresa could look through her, knowing every thought in the girl's head before she had spoken a word. It was this curious superiority that kept Helena away out of pride. It was Helena's wish to be first in everything—in beauty, in ugliness, in good, and in evil. And because of her pride this girl—possessed with so much beauty in body and soul, so fired with genius, a rich and crowded life before her—could not have the pleasure of showing off her great sufferings before the old woman, nor of impressing her with her flexibility of mind or her depth of emotion.

Theresa knew the Polish masters Slowacki and Mickiewicz as well as the German poets Schiller and Goethe almost by heart, and long before Helena discovered William Shakespeare and reveled in *Hamlet, The Merchant of Venice,* or *Two Gentlemen of Verona,* the old aunt knew Shakespeare through and through. And if Helena recited and forgot a line, it was Theresa who prompted her and without hesitation. Theresa had an instinctive knowledge of the world's ways, and she knew the pitfalls that lay in the girl's path. She sensed that Helena was destined to great achievement and longed to help her, to guide her away from all pain. Too late, the dying Theresa was coming to realize that she could love this headstrong girl more than she loved her God, and it pleased her to say so aloud many times before the shocked Gustav Sinnemayer.

Gradually an unspoken bond grew up between the two. As Helena secretly struggled to impress the old lady with her startling knowledge of history and literature, Theresa allowed herself to indicate approval by a quick nod of the head, as she did also when Helena sang the songs of Schubert or acted the parts of Louise in *Kabale und Liebe,* Gretchen in *Faust,* or Klärchen Marchen in *Egmont* before some public gathering. And Helena knew, too, that it was only because of the powerful sympathy of her great aunt that her escape from the convent had been passed over without too much stir.

At this time there lived in Cracow a well-known actor and music teacher by the name of Herr Axtman, who by order of the guardian angel Sinnemayer taught Helena singing and dramatic diction. Herr Axtman was of the opinion that his pupil should take up a singing career rather than go on the dramatic stage. The whole family agreed with him with the exception of

Aunt Theresa and Helena herself. Helena had decided to keep peace over the matter for a while, at least until the memory of her convent escapade had become dim. Furthermore, she liked to sing. But Aunt Theresa was not content to let it pass. She expressed her opinion openly that since Gustav was spending the money anyway, it would be better for the girl to be sent to Fritz Devrient, the handsome, curly-headed actor, famous for his extraordinary portrayal of Hamlet.

The argument was settled again in Theresa's favor, but only because Herr Axtman obtained a much desired engagement and left Cracow.

Aunt Theresa worried about her niece, and observed her far more carefully than Helena had thought. Since that Eve of St. John, Helena had seen Igo far more often than she wanted her family to know.

This was a time when she was thankful for her ability to act, for she made each meeting seem as though it was something casual—something almost accidental. Her family was unanimous in its denunciation of Igo. After all, what was he! A dreamer, an artist, a nobody who would drift through life. He was not for their Helena. And Sinnemayer, had he known everything, would have been violent in his disapproval.

One murky morning, Theresa approached the girl and beckoned her into her room. Once inside, Theresa shot the bolt and turned to look at Helena with penetrating eyes. Helena sat down, trying to appear calm. The aunt minced no words.

"You are in love with Igo! Perhaps you are even planning to go so far as to marry him?"

Helena grew paler than the covers of her chair. For the first time in her life, her ready wit failed. Theresa pulled her chair closer. She gave the girl no chance to make up an answer.

"How do I know? I have watched. I know you too well, Helena. But do you think I will let you marry him? To let him destroy your career! Do you think that your family would let you?" She sat back, waiting.

But the girl continued her silence, her eyes filling with tears, as the old woman proceeded with an almost fierce directness.

"I want you to understand that my desire is to help you. Igo is no good. I know these artists. Ha! They promise to marry you. They'll promise anything in their dreams. And then what happens! They take *advantage*. They take advantage of a young girl's passion." She shook her head, laying her wrinkled old hand on the girl's arm.

"Helena, Helena! I am the only one who understands you, and for your sake you must tell me everything. You must trust me to help you. I grow weaker every day. My body is already half in the grave. There is not much time."

Helena burst out into a loud cry, burying her face in the folds of the chair. Theresa waited in silence, apparently unimpressed by the girl's sobs. When Helena quieted down, Theresa began again:

"I know well that whatever you have done was done in love for Igo, but I know too that you love the theatre, and that Igo is too poor to be able to help you become the great actress you want to be. Any children you may have can only be an impediment. Since you have no money of your own, it is only a miracle that can save you from tragic failure. On the other hand, if your will is strong, as I think it is, you will overcome this first love of yours as well as any other difficulties. What use will your life be to you without your art? The beauty and greatness of art must flow by the force of money."

Cutting off her speech abruptly, the old woman settled down in expectation of the girl's confession. But Helena's weeping died away into silence. Minutes passed without a word being spoken. Beyond the window the passing wagons rumbled over the cobblestones, and the children playing in the streets laughed and screamed. The minute hand of Theresa's clock moved down to the quarter hour. But the silence continued.

This silence brought Theresa for the first time face to face with Helena's strong will. Theresa was not even sure of the effect of her plain speaking, although her guess was that Helena had already chosen another method of solving her problem, and wanted to talk to no one about it.

Without warning, Theresa straightened her shriveled frame, turned, and left the room. She reasoned that, if she left the girl alone for half an hour or so and returned, she would then find her quite ready to talk and to listen to the wisdom of her aunt.

But the plan failed. When Theresa returned it was to find her room empty.

Theresa kept her secret to herself, knowing well the scenes that would follow were the girl's mother to learn. For the next few days, on the pretext of working about the house, Theresa made every effort to corner Helena once more, but the girl kept out of her way. She traced Helena's activities out of the house and found that she was seeing Igo at every opportunity. Theresa's anxiety grew with the thought that the young people might be planning a sudden marriage. How could Helena understand the full extent of such a tragedy?

All at once, weakened by anxiety, old Theresa took a turn for the worse, and was forced to retire to her bed. She lost all hope of saving Helena from marriage to Igo. It would mean for the girl—living a pitiful existence, perhaps at most the member of a provincial troupe, caring for her child, posing for Igo, their comedy of love finishing up somewhere in a cold and wretched attic. There was nothing Theresa could do now to save her unless Helena herself should decide to visit Theresa's room alone. She came several times, but always when someone else was present, and always she was very silent, avoiding her aunt's pleading eyes. How could Theresa speak before the others? Bitter wailing and recriminations would possess the house, and Helena in her pride would march out of the house to Igo, and so fulfill the saying that every calf will find its slaughterer. Theresa cursed such proverbs as being not the wisdom but the stupidity of peoples.

Time slowly advanced, pulling long and tiresome hours like an old horse straining at the plow. Theresa felt as though buried under the black furrows of minutes. She lay in the silence of her room trying to reason out how long she had to live. She knew her strength was going. She had no hope to sustain her. Her death would cause no commotion. The sorrow of the household would come only after she was gone. The house would remain for days uncleaned, the linen unpressed, the meals served sloppily by the cook. Yes, then they would think of her, and they would be sorry—all of them, Felix, Adolph, Josephine, Helena, and their mother.

But no. She excluded Helena. Helena was different. Helena

loved her now, loved her in her own wild manner, even if pride kept her at a distance.

As the dying woman lay in her bed thinking these thoughts, she became aware of a faint knocking on the door. Was it an answer to the prayers in her heart? The door opened. As the old woman's eyes turned in surprise, Helena stepped in, quiet as a spirit, dressed in a long pink robe with edges of lace. She sat on the chair beside her aunt's bed and silently gazed into the old, tired face. Theresa's eyes had turned back to the ceiling, and she now stretched out a thin hand, found the girl's fingers, and pressed them weakly.

A few minutes passed in silence, before Helena began in a whisper, "I have decided to marry Sinnemayer at once."

Theresa's eyes narrowed quickly. When she looked at Helena, her lined face almost as pale as the pillow itself, the eyes were wide and burning. The old gleam of triumph had returned.

"I knew you would come. I knew, I knew. . . . You are a wise girl. Remember that God has given all to all, but not all to one. Sinnemayer will marry you without fail. Gustav is kind. Be good to him. You will see."

Helena lowered her head so that her face was hidden by the fall of her long hair, glowing copper in the light of the sinking sun. With her hands she reached out to the cold bones of her aunt's fingers. But the old woman's gaze was held by the gleaming blue of a fly in the corner trapped in a gray web. The spider was slowly approaching its victim. The clock's beating heart and the wild buzz of the fly were the only sounds in this stately room, hung with old tapestries and pictures in tarnished frames.

When Theresa spoke it was in a whisper. It was almost as if she were afraid lest the spider be distracted by her voice. "Leave it all to me, and don't worry any more. I will arrange everything with your Gustav. It will bring happiness to him when I tell him how it is to be."

The old woman's voice died away. The fly buzzed desperately in the corner of the ceiling. The threads of its trap broke suddenly and the fly swung free, dropped, and stunned itself against the windowpane. Outside, a burning sun was dancing its departure on the roof tops and on the heads of the evergreens. The sun is forever young, thought Theresa, in this part of the

country, and always ready to break out into a mazurek, like the
people who live in these Carpathian Mountains.

"Helena." The voice of Theresa was at once firm and sharp.
"Open the window." Helena did as she was told without a word
and returned to her chair. But Theresa was not finished. "Open
the closet. You will find a carved chest there, under those dresses
and shoes. It was your father who gave it to me some thirty
years ago on my birthday. Bring it over here."

Helena found the chest. It was of dark red wood, carved in
flowers and covered with a sheeting of silver, and remarkably
heavy, yet not too large to lift onto the bed as Theresa wanted it.

"Open it," commanded Theresa. Inside there was foreign
money, gold and silver. "Spread it out on the bed cover beside
me." Silently, Helena scooped the money out, and her face lit
up with excitement as she came upon strings of pearls, a dia-
mond necklace, and several rings.

"This is my wedding present to you. It's all yours," said
Theresa decisively.

The girl's face was full of wonder and astonishment. "I am
not worthy of all these riches. I'm not worthy."

"Nonsense, girl. If you're not so already, then you will be so
shortly." And she reached up and touched the girl's cheek. "Of
the whole household you are the one worthy, for you are the
most beautiful, and jewelry is made for you. As for the money,
it will be useful when you go out into the world full of burdens
and cares, and you will thank me for it then."

6. THE FAIR DEAL

GUSTAV SINNEMAYER found one more reason for worshipping Goethe. He was reading of the sufferings of Werther, the ideal lover, when the miracle occurred. Helena said "Yes," and even agreed on a wedding without delay. Helena was beautiful and young, vivid and full of energy, while he was twenty years older and quite unattractive. Every day he said that to himself as he stared frowning into his mirror. Of course he had money. But what of that, when Count Potocki, known as the King of Cracow, was quite openly paying attention to the dazzling Helena during their promenades in the Botanical Gardens.

What if the Count had learned of Helena's condition? That would not have deterred him. One chance at snapping up this talented beauty whose fame was already spreading beyond the bounds of Cracow, and he would have left his Catherine flat. There were plenty of rumors to that effect, and Gustav had not missed them. There had been several invitations from the dignified mother of the young Count, presumably through a desire to look Helena over. But now, quite suddenly, the great Goethe had performed a miracle. It was not the delicate, passionate Igo nor the persistent Count who had won the day, but he, Gustav Sinnemayer.

Gustav was quite aware that the crafty manipulations of Theresa might also have had something to do with the result, but this could not be verified. He preferred to think mystically and to credit Goethe. The romanticism of Werther had profoundly affected him. He had made up his mind that if Helena refused his last proposal, he would end all in true Wertherian style—by suicide. He saw no other alternative. What hope was there that he would ever fall in love again? And without love he would never give his riches to another woman, no matter if she were ten times more beautiful and more talented. So he had told himself. And now she was his.

Gustav was convinced that he understood Helena's soul. For he had helped bring her up, opened her mind and heart to the riches of culture, spent long hours with her almost every day, guiding her, encouraging her. Yes, he understood her soul, and that was extremely important. He could never bring himself to live with anyone else whose every inner response he could not know. And as for the child, he rather blamed himself for that. With a quick marriage, no one would know.

He recalled the advice of Theresa: "A rider pats the horse before he saddles it." Yes, Gustav thought, he would treat Helena with great care, watching over her closely but with tenderness. Slowly he would train her. Slowly she would come to depend upon him for all she needed. And he made up his mind that no power on earth would ever take Helena away from him, and that love would never make a fool out of him.

Gustav acted swiftly. There was to be no hitch in his plans now. First he announced that theirs was to be a quiet wedding attended only by the members of the family. It led to an immediate outcry. Helena's mother began to storm. She accused him of being a miser. Meanwhile, the girl's three half-brothers and her brother called a meeting of their own. They refused to attend the ceremony unless it was done in proper lavish style. They went so far as to offer financial assistance. But this time, the usually quiet and polite Gustav came out with a defiant "No," for which he offered no explanation. His position was quite unassailable, since Helena stood firmly by his decision.

It happened that Josephine was the only one who suspected more than avarice or any other reason for Gustav's haste. She spoke with a knowing smile, refusing to side with her family: "Of course they want to have their own home as fast as possible for they want to be happily married without anyone else butting in."

One by one, the family surrendered to the inevitable, putting all resentment aside. Each in a different way found happiness in the Church of the Virgin Mary, as they listened to the chant of the officiating priest. Only Helena, standing erect and motionless beside Gustav, in the long white gown that had once been Theresa's, could feel no happiness.

Her ears heard nothing of the priest's words. Her eyes fixed on his white-robed chest saw nothing of the tall lean apostles carved out of wood by the famous fifteenth-century artist Wit Stwosz, who had gathered them there for the Coronation of the Virgin Queen. Helena had loved the work of this artist, even from childhood, but on this day her thoughts were far away. The great waters of the Vistula were flowing in her mind, and the words and the music of the ceremony were lost. A gentle breeze had played among the grasses kissed by the moon upon that unforgettable night of Saint John. Helena was overcome with a strange faintness, and unthinkingly she clutched Gustav's arm for support. But her face, shining with a beauty as cold as that of the face of the Virgin over the altar, betrayed nothing of her thoughts.

"Be the will of God. . . ." The words from the ceremony began to cut into her thoughts. Marriage to Gustav was, to Helena, the supreme penitence for her sins. And again white lips murmured: "Be the will of God. . . ." Then the cold sensation of gold on her finger pierced like a sword into the past. Helena came to and forced a smile upon the mask of her face. This was the end of a frivolous period in her life and the beginning of what was to be a great performance. And she now belonged to this man whose task it was to teach her the meaning of life and art. The law decreed that she must follow his teachings, be with him in sorrow and in joy.

After the ceremony Gustav and Helena returned to the house to find that, in spite of their wishes, Madame Opid had prepared a farewell party. She had invited over sixty relations and friends, and spared no expense for rare Polish whiskies, imported French wines, several dozen varieties of delicacies, fish in colorful sauces, and desserts prepared from the fruits of the South. A clinking of glasses greeted the bride as she entered, shouts of congratulations and well-wishing, as the music crashed into a gay dance. Overcome with happiness, Madame Opid gave orders to the servants hired for this great celebration to go out to the crowd of Cracow's beggars, who stood in the street in smiling expectation, to give them food and drink, together with the sum of twenty-five florins, so that their prayers would launch the newly married couple upon a joyful future.

Gustav sat with the bride in the center of the room, empty-

ing one glass after another of Theresa's long-cherished cognac.
Helena smiled and sipped and slightly tipped her flowered head
in response to all the compliments, but everyone was far too
full of noise and laughter to notice how really reserved she was.
The five-piece orchestra played incessantly with more energy
than skill through the sentimental songs of Schubert, the polonaise, the oberek, mazurek, and kujawiak, then back again to
the classics. Servants rushed in and out, piling up the plates as
soon as they were empty with kielbasas of all varieties, hams,
fish, mountains of bread, and pastries. The incessant flow of
food and bottles made it look as if the festivities would go on
into the second day.

By seven in the morning Gustav was quite befuddled, but
something in his brain nudged him to get up, take his bride by
the hand, and make a pretense of sneaking out of the noisy
rooms into the street. But their departure was hardly unnoticed
by the less intoxicated who winked and laughed, while some
rushed to the door in time to see the coach drive off.

Fifteen minutes later, the coach drew up at Number 21
Grodzka Street, and Gustav carefully let himself out. Helena
looked tired and was very silent as he helped her down, trying
to see that she didn't spoil her long blue velvet dress and cloak.
"Now you will see the home I have prepared for you," he
whispered into her ear as he pressed to her arm, as if for support. His eyes were glassy, his breath hot with liquor. Gustav
rarely took a drink, but on this day of his success he had not
been able to resist the temptation. He felt it important now to
conceal the fact that he had taken too much. Her silence was
disturbing, and he repeated as they approached the house, "Now
you will see the home I have prepared for you." Then he stopped
her and spoke very gravely. "Don't think I am drunk. I know
what I'm saying, and what I'm doing. You will see I have done
everything to make you happy."

Now he stood in front of the door, trying to open it. Helena
stood beside him without speaking for a moment. Then she
said quietly, "If that is so, Gustav, why haven't you changed
your name as you promised you would?"

Gustav abandoned his struggle with the obstinate door, and
straightened himself as if suddenly sobering. He spoke aloud

now like a child boasting. "I did, I did. The marriage certificate bears the name Gustav Sinnemayer Modrzejewski. And from now on I'll be signing my name simply G. S. Modrzejewski. You see I wanted to give it to you as a wedding present, so I did it on the eve of our wedding. You didn't want to have a German name. You told me long ago. I did not forget, my dear."

Helena uttered a delighted cry and threw her arms around his neck. She kissed his ear and cheek and met his lips as she began trembling with emotion. "Oh, how kind you are! Oh, how . . ." She pressed so impetuously against him that he found himself pushed back against the door.

He managed to find breath enough to explain, "I changed my name only as a great sacrifice, only because you wanted it. I didn't want to hear you say to me again, 'Do I have to carry this awful name?' No, my dear, I want you to speak well of me always, and you will see how much I'm prepared to do for you."

Helena smothered him with her kisses so that he could hardly have said more. His eyes became moist and his face red with emotion. His hands trembled. He clutched at her, jerking his whole weight against the door, trying to regain his equilibrium. The door flew open. He lurched back and would have fallen with Helena on top of him, if she had not seized hold of the door knob and grabbed Gustav by the neck.

"Damn and blast!" yelled Gustav hoarsely.

But Helena hushed him up. "Don't scream so. You'll wake up the servants."

"Ah, the servants," he recovered himself, blinking, and began to concentrate on the idea. "Oh, the servants? I got rid of them for the whole day."

Helena closed the door, and began tugging him by the arm into the newly decorated living room. With characteristic good humor and forgiveingness she knew that her husband had celebrated too freely at his own wedding, and she wanted him only to rest before he collapsed in a stupor. But Gustav suddenly pulled himself together.

"No, no! Not on the couch! The bed is what we want. In the next room. . . ." His sentence exploded into nervous laughter. He was trying to act the part of a young and impetuous bridegroom, and clumsily he hauled Helena along with him.

He threw her on the bed, ripping at her clothes, covering her with drunken, well-intentioned kisses. But gradually his passion decreased. He fumbled awkwardly until finally he sank back with a bitter cry.

"Not now . . . Not now . . . I can't . . . The drink!"

He turned from the lovely girl, and began to sob. His shoulders heaved, his hands pressed against his perspiring face.

Several hours passed when Helena stirred awake and realized that she had been asleep. She sat up, and began to take off her soundly sleeping husband's shoes. She pulled the bed clothes over him and tucked him in. That first wedding day Gustav spent in the deep slumber of a man who had exhausted himself, his moustache, mussed through kissing, now moving evenly with each loud breath.

Helena could not sleep again that night, and for several nights in succession she lay awake while her husband slept. Then one night she sat up in bed and wrote in her diary:

"The days are not mine, but the nights are. When all the household is asleep, I get up and go to the window. I open it and lean out into the moonlight, into the night of stars. I stretch my arms wide and breathe deeply. The nightingale sings and I smell the perfume of the acacias. I am filled with indescribable delight and sadness. Then I wish that I had wings so that I could fly out into endless space. But why am I so moved? Does the idea of becoming a great actress bring so much joy to me? I do not know. For while it does bring happiness to me, there is also there a mysterious anguish. What is the matter with me? I must leave my country. I must go on the German stage, and be among strangers. Yes. That is my destiny. I will go.

"How I wish I could speak English! I would play Ophelia. I would play Portia, and Juliet. Gradually peace comes over me, as I think of the roles I shall play. I half-close my eyes, until I see among the trees and the shrubs—Louise wringing her hands and weeping, Ophelia and her vacant looks, Margaret in the arms of Faust, Klarchen addressing the mob in desperate accents. And all these phantoms, though quite unlike each other, still have the same face, changed only by the expression, and it is my own face. My thoughts fly off into the future and I see

myself on the stage. I hear the applause from the people. I see
their tears and smiles. I make them feel what I feel. This is
power . . . ! Oh, no, no! This is all a dream, a delusion! What
does my miserable life amount to? Where am I going? What
will become of me?"

7. ON A SLIPPERY ROAD

THE HASTE of the marriage of Helena and Gustav, together with the premature birth of a son, Rudolph, had caused enough gossip in Cracow to last for a long time. But almost immediately a new storm broke over their heads. It was on a morning in May of 1861 that Mrs. Martha Pilch, returning from her shopping with fresh rolls and milk, found something truly remarkable lying in the road in front of the Modrzejewski residence. Since Mrs. Pilch lived right opposite, it was easy for her to pick it up and carry it into her own apartment. She worked over it hastily, pasting the torn pieces together and cleaning off the dirt. Then, right after breakfast, she called all her friends in to look at the find. It was an oil painting of Helena and her baby son.

The women in the market place and in the salons, the professional gossip-mongers in the cafés, the whole city, it seemed, whispered and exclaimed about the story. Pieces of the incident were fitted together, like the torn canvas of the picture. The young artist had painted the picture from memory, it was said. He had sent it by special messenger as a gift for the young *madonna* Modrzejewski. But when her husband had returned home from a conference with the director of the theatre, and found the painting hanging on the wall in their bedroom, he had snatched it off the wall and in a fit of rage torn it to pieces and unwisely thrown it out of the window. According to one version, he had even beaten his wife when she had tried to resist. Others had it that a duel had occurred between the insulted husband and the young painter, and that the latter was recuperating from a pistol wound in his home at Krzemionki. Obvious deductions began to be made about the relationship between Igo, Helena, and the four-month-old baby Rudolph. Some expressed compassion for Gustav, others ridicule.

The city had its brand-new sensation, and the Modrzejewskis were made to feel as uncomfortable as possible. Through the main entrance of their house appeared prominent but uninvited guests, while the kitchen entrance became a hangout for men and women who claimed to be friends of the cook. Both groups were clearly there to spy upon the beautiful girl and her jealous husband. They were pointed out in the streets by people who made abusive hissing noises with their mouths and by others who followed snickering. Count Potocki's mother grew more curious than ever to see this much-talked-about girl. Swallowing the gossip, hook, line, and sinker, she sent off her friend Mr. Rembowski to invite the young actress to dinner.

Gustav and Helena refused all such invitations and went out as little as possible, but they were constantly plagued with visitors, and the fury of tongues increased. Their only recourse was to leave Cracow for a while. The coach was prepared one late afternoon, and Gustav, Helena, and Rudolph drove west for the small town of Bochnia, some fifty miles away.

Gustav owned land in Bochnia and several apartment houses, and he had shares there in the old salt mines. He decided that he would convert all these into cash. Then they would go abroad. Gustav's belief in the acting genius of his wife was as strong as his love for the works of Goethe. It was high time, he felt, that Helena was seen on the stages of Vienna and Berlin and Paris.

They had traveled little more than twenty miles when they ran into a fearful storm. The rain came down in sheets with the wind sweeping full at them, until the horses were blinded. They slipped and lurched in the soggy mire of the road, the coachman wildly yelling and lashing his whip. The poor man was soaked to the skin. He could see nothing ahead of him, and knew well the dangers of trying to go on if the storm continued. At last he leaned down to suggest that they rest at the nearest inn.

Gustav agreed at once, but this did not satisfy Helena. She had been gripping the side of the lurching coach with one hand and the baby's crib with the other, her face set in a mask of determination. Now she protested, "Gustav, I don't think we should stop just because of a storm."

"But, my dear, the horses are drowning in the mud. And what of Kalasanty? He's not made of stone."

"Oh yes, I didn't think of him. Well, why can't he tie the reins to the coach and sit with us? Don't you think the horses could go by themselves?"

Gustav would have laughed, if he hadn't felt annoyed. "Impossible. And what is your reason for wanting to travel in such a flood?"

Helena was given no time to think up a good reason, for the coach had come to an abrupt halt. Out of the window she saw a brightly lit house. The horses made no effort to go on, the coachman no effort to persuade them. Already a bearded man had hurried out to them and was opening the coach door with the words: "A guest in the inn is God in the inn." They got out and hurriedly entered the place, leaving Kalasanty to lead the tired horses to the stable.

The rain did not let up. The wind rose till it howled in the treetops, fierce as the wolf packs in the Kampinowska forest.

Some few travelers already occupied the large room of the inn, drying their clothes in front of the big earthen fireplace. The sight of a woman and child, and the obvious importance of the guests, caused a commotion among these folk who were peasants and treated the aristocracy with a marked respect born of fear. There was a hurried scramble for the still wet clothing. But Gustav paid no attention to them and hurried Helena through the large smoke-filled room. The innkeeper was opening the door of a side room. Helena went in and saw two beds, a table and chairs, and a large picture of Christ on the Cross lit up by a kerosene lamp. She smelled the scent of fresh violets bursting from an earthen vase on the table.

The innkeeper, standing at the door, caught her eye and bowed low. "The best room in the house for your worships."

"Won't you bring us some boiled milk," she said, "for the child, and some bread and kielbasa with tea for us?"

"Most certainly, most illustrious lady," said the man, bowing low again, his eyes glancing into his hand at the few florins Gustav had just slipped to him. He smiled and left in a hurry, closing the door behind him.

Rudolph began to cry. Gustav stared down at him, as Helena busied herself with changing his clothes.

"I can't understand why you didn't bring the nurse Mania

with you," complained Gustav. "She would be a great help to us in Bochnia. She should be tending to the child now. Not you, Helena. You're tired."

But Helena shook her head. "I'm not tired. And it'll be time enough to have the servants with us when we know where we're going to live."

He looked closely at her. "Why do you say you're not tired. Your hands are shaking."

She glanced quickly up at him, as if she were seized by some fear. "I am a bit cold," was all she said. Only after wrapping the child up in a warm blanket did she add, "Some hot tea will warm me up."

But Gustav was silent. He had asked the question merely to put himself at ease, for they had hardly spoken a word during the greater part of the trip. He knew she was against leaving Cracow. With every mile on the road he knew her depression increased. He felt that something strange was happening to her, but he knew better than to speak of it. They might get into an argument over Igo again. Helena had insisted that everything connected with that name belonged to the past. He guessed that she thought about Igo constantly even against her will. It was as if the young artist had marred their future with black paint. It touched everything and could not be wiped off. It invaded their thoughts. Gustav had counted on the passage of time. He had thought that the move from Cracow would have its effect. Instead she was plunged into the deepest gloom. She treated Gustav with a measured politeness that he instinctively feared.

"Time will cure her," he said to himself repeatedly, but it was more to convince himself. It was like an incantation to ward off the curse of Igo. He felt within himself that he could have murdered his instrusive rival with a clear conscience. When he watched Helena's suffering, his mind would turn with ease to the thought of murder, plotting some swift and silent end for Igo that would never be discovered—perhaps by drowning in the Vistula. At times when his wife would smile at him or be more talkative, these dark thoughts would vanish, leaving a certain sensation behind, like the present odor of smoke seeping in from the large room of the inn.

There was a knock. He went to the door and the innkeeper
with the help of a rosy-cheeked girl brought in the food. Then
the innkeeper backed to the door again, nudging the girl out
with his elbow. "Everything your worships ordered." He bowed
low once more. "Should your worships desire something further, we beg you just to knock on the door. The girl will be
there on watch to be at your service. Perhaps some wine or
some whisky? . . ."

But Gustav turned away. "That's all for tonight," he said
drily.

The door closed. Almost at once there was the sound of scuf-
fling outside, and the next minute it was thrown open again
with such wild power that the house shook. Two men stood
just inside the room wearing black hoods over their heads with
slit holes for their eyes.

"Hand over your money and valuables," commanded one, as
he moved nearer to Helena, a long knife in his hand. The other
man held two pistols and remained at the door. In the large
room beyond, the innkeeper and the peasants lay full length on
the floor by the fireplace. Pale and speechless, Gustav and Helena produced their valuables, Gustav his wallet and Helena the
jewelry she was wearing. The man snatched them and rammed
them into his pockets. "More," he snapped.

Gustav took a step back which put him a little behind his wife.
"We have no more," he said hoarsely.

With a cry of rage, the man hurled Helena out of his way
and rushed at Gustav, knife upraised. Gustav grappled with
him desperately; in his fear he showed more strength than he
knew he possessed. The man's hood slipped down, and Helena
snatched up the tea and threw the scalding liquid into his face.
The knife aimed at Gustav's throat came down into his arm,
where it remained. The bandit turned with a howl of agony,
clutching at his face, and made for the door. His companion
fired point-blank at Gustav and fled.

With the bandits gone, the peasants came pouring into the
room, where Gustav and Helena lay unconscious by the bed.
The child was screaming pitifully. No one seemed to know what
to do. It was Rudolph's screams that seemed to bring Helena
back to her senses. She sat up and stared at Gustav. Blood was

seeping out of his knife wound. She crawled over to him and ripped his shirt away at the arm. The peasants stood around shaking helplessly. Only the innkeeper had the presence of mind to help Helena. By a miracle the bullet had missed its mark. The knife wound was not deep. Gustav had merely fainted from shock.

"Throw some cold water on his face," Helena whispered.

The innkeeper helped her bandage up the arm. A peasant came in with a pail and respectfully spilled the water on Gustav's face, holding the pail high in the air as he watched the result. Gustav gasped and opened his eyes. Helena propped his head up on her lap, as he looked about him with veiled eyes.

"Why did he want to kill me?" he murmured, his pale lips moving, wet with the water, and his eyes closed again.

Helena wiped his face lightly. "Everything will be all right." She felt too tired to think of anything else to say.

Two peasants now helped to place Gustav on the bed, and his wife sat beside him, paying no attention to the crying child. The rosy-cheeked girl came into the room, picked up the child, and pressed him to her breast. She sat on the bed opposite, rocking him in her arms until the screaming died slowly away.

The peasants remained in the room, but the general mood had changed. In loud voices, as if they aimed to be heard by the Modrzejewskis, they talked of the robbery. Some had witnessed bandit raids of this kind before, but of these two bandits one was dressed in peasant clothes while the one with the guns wore city clothes, with his boots shining, untouched by rain. The innkeeper jerked his head. "And why," he asked, "after getting the money and the jewels should they want to kill innocent people?"

"Only the gentleman," put in the servant girl, with a glance toward Gustav.

Gustav suddenly turned his head toward Helena and stared into her face, as if he could pry open some answer to the mystery.

Helena could feel his burning, suspicious eyes upon her, but she did not turn to him, and sat motionless as silent tears began to roll down her cheeks.

8. THROUGH THE BACKSTAGE

MR. LOBOJKO was a handsome man of many talents. He was tall and dark, with blue eyes. His hair was slickly combed. No one knew where he came from to this small town of Bochnia, and no one knew his age. It was guessed that he must be in his early forties. He was far too energetic, too effervescent to be older. His fame spread through the district, for in the week of his arrival he joined in the annual dance festival that was held in the fields beyond the town, and acquitted himself with such skill that he stood out as a master among amateurs. He danced all the ladies and the young impressionable girls into a whirl, especially with his masterly quadrille. They liked his compliments, his smile, and the cut of his clothes in the very latest Vienna style. The men of Bochnia were won over more slowly, but Mr. Lobojko worked on them with a purpose, with expansive gestures, with his endless fistfuls of florins, treating any and all to drinks on sight.

Through the weeks that followed, when all the enthusiastic gossip about the new arrival had somewhat spent itself, it had to be admitted that little was known about him, how he lived, what had been the reason of his coming, and even what his first name was. He, on the other hand, hailed everyone by his first name, and almost without effort it seemed, knew who did what, who was in the money, and who slept with whom.

His accomplishments were extraordinarily varied. He was an excellent photographer, and as a teacher had a flair for mathematics, but it was the stage which interested him primarily, as a director, as an actor, as a dancer, and with an acute sense of the business end of production.

The arrival of Gustav Sinnemayer Modrzejewski and his beautiful wife in this legend-wrapped town, famous for its salt mines, was of interest enough to a large proportion of its three thousand inhabitants to interest Mr. Lobojko exceedingly. The day of their arrival he greeted Gustav, whom he at once addressed as "Gustav," with a flattering interest so that the latter was completely won over. By the next day, Gustav was priding himself on his quick recognition of Mr. Lobojko's talents, and Mr. Lobojko was seen leaving the office of the local theatre with a smile on his face that was broad enough to be surprising even for him. He had arranged for an appearance of Helena Modrzejewska in Gustav's favorite play of Schiller's, *Kabale und Liebe.*

Mr. Lobojko, much enriched by the transaction, saw himself importing some famous actors, such as Fritz Devrient from Vienna or Monsieur Checinski from Warsaw. Gustav, for his part, was picturing Bochnia as a new center of theatrical art where Helena's fame would grow and grow, until all Europe would turn its face to an obscure town among the salt mines where the great German classic plays were being presented by a brilliant and beautiful actress.

The only obstacle to Gustav's plans was Helena herself, who swiftly turned from Schiller to Shakespeare, and won such applause that she decided that only Shakespeare could do justice to her talents. She divided her time between caring for her young son and the study of the Shakespearean roles, and thought little of anything else. When Gustav proceeded to organize a theatrical group under the name of The New Sandec Company at great expense to himself, she protested: "It's a waste of time and money to concentrate all your attentions on Bochnia. If you really do want to help me in my career, Gustav, take me to Vienna. Spend your money there, where there are good actors, good theatres, and critics and audiences that know their stage."

But Gustav had a strong card in his favor. It was Mr. Lobojko. Gustav was quick to see how much Helena admired the man for his energy and skill. She would more easily be persuaded by Mr. Lobojko's advice. He thereupon conferred with Mr. Lobojko, a price was set for the man's services, and Mr. Lobojko at once became an indispensable friend of the family.

Mr. Lobojko's persuasiveness was both delicate and pressing at the same instant, as he repeatedly dwelled upon the sensationalism and the romanticism of Helena Modrzejewska of Bochnia, rising up, a new star on the horizon, and a star from among the

people, attracting the great actors of the world to visit Bochnia
for the chance of playing opposite her, enticing the critics from
Vienna, from Berlin, from Warsaw. No more would there be
the need to go to Berlin or Vienna to seek an audience with
some second-rate director of some small theatre to beg an opportunity to show her talent. The greatest would seek her out
after her debut at Casino Hall in Bochnia.

"Lobojko will fix everything," Gustav repeated over and
over, with an honest enthusiasm. "He is a manager, director,
and actor of superb qualities. You know that yourself, Helena.
You told me yourself. Trust him. He knows what is best for
you."

Yet secretly he knew in his heart that he did not trust Lobojko, despite his need of the man's services. This Lobojko, he
knew, had designs of his own on Helena. He had to be watched.
Perhaps it was reckless to trust him as far as he did. But there
was one weakness in the man's make-up—his love of money.
Lobojko loved money more than he would love any woman.

Gustav had money, ready money, plenty of it. He was selling
his Bochnia properties and his share in the salt mine. And this
he must do—anything to keep Helena from Vienna. This much
he had decided, for now he was afraid. Helena was too beautiful, too impetuous. They would court her in Vienna. They
would turn her head. They would fall in love with her, and
break down her resistance by subtle means. Helena was so
young, so inexperienced, still only a child. He, Gustav, must
protect her, keep her at his side, until maturity made her realize
that no one could ever love her as much as he did, regardless of
his physical shortcomings.

One evening after dinner, Helena surprised the two men
with the declaration that she had decided to put on the French
light opera *The White Camellia,* in which she would sing the
main part, the proceeds to go to the orphanage of the town.

Gustav was delighted over this sudden interest in Bochnia's
welfare, and he turned to Lobojko with a smile. "Now you will
see what a beautiful mezzo-soprano we have on our hands,
Lobojko!"

Helena was made a trifle uneasy by this enthusiasm. "I'm not doing this to show off my voice. I'm only doing it to help the poor children."

Mr. Lobojko insisted on flattery. "It is not only your voice that will please. It is enough just to see you on the stage, Madame."

"Nevertheless," argued Helena with some irritation, "I was thinking of the orphans when I looked over the stage of the Casino this afternoon. It's not a bad stage, at all."

Smiling, Gustav hastened to pour more of his expensive wine into Lobojko's glass. As he did so the thought came to him: "The wine means nothing. His staying so much at the house means nothing. But why have I dumped so much money into this man's lap, when perhaps I could have managed without him?" But aloud he said mildly, "And perhaps we will choose something from Schiller as our next offering, eh?"

"Yes, something from Schiller," echoed Lobojko, examining the color of the wine as if comparing it with the brightness of Helena's hair.

Helena remarked drily, "Or perhaps again something for the benefit of the orphanage."

Gustav could find nothing that would fill up the silence which followed, and he poured more wine for himself and his guest. Then Helena continued, "I will invite my sister Josephine and her fiance. They both have very good voices, and could be of great help."

Gustav rubbed the bald spot of his head, as if encouraging bright words. "Mr. Lobojko might help out, too, Helena. He's got a fine voice as well as being such an excellent actor."

"Perhaps," said Helena shortly, throwing a smile at Lobojko.

Though Helena still insisted Schiller could wait until she got to Vienna, Gustav remained satisfied in having his way on every other issue. Helena followed *The White Camellia* with a Polish operetta, and followed that with Victor Hugo's *Marie Tudor* and Konstanty Majeranowski's *Dwory Polskie*. All were a glorious success with the Bochnia audiences. Under the watchful eye of Gustav, she toured the towns in Podkarpacie, in so-called "Galicia," from west to east, until she arrived at Lwow. There, at the Waly Hetmanskie Theatre, she evoked the exuberant admiration of a very selective audience. But still the promises of her husband and Lobojko did not materialize.

What did it matter to Helena if her acting talent and her beauty were raved about in the local papers, when nothing was heard from beyond the districts she toured? Her fame had not spread, as they promised, throughout Europe. It had not even spread throughout the Austro-Hungarian Empire. Her own certainty of future greatness and her all-powerful ambition to reach the very top of fame had by no means dimmed, but all her efforts were nothing but seed sown upon rocks if they brought forth no invitations from the European capitals.

Helena returned to Bochnia, and to her son, in a strange mood of quietness. A firm decision was growing within her to take her future into her own hands.

Gustav was worried. He had the unaccountable sensation that the reins were slipping out of his hands. There was Lobojko. Something had happened to him. He was abruptly transformed. From the elegant, vivacious, smiling man of vast capabilities he became solemn, uncommunicative, almost brooding, forgetful and—wonder of wonders—careless in his dress. It was as if some terrible knowledge were consuming him. It had the effect of arousing an odd kind of sympathy for him. There was something more natural about him, even though Gustav was finding him far less pleasant as company. All this Gustav could have accepted with equanimity if it had not been that the man was quite obviously seeking out excuses to spend as much time as possible in the house to be with Helena. The main reason, of course, was the search through the classics of European literature for new roles for Helena and, incidentally, for himself to play.

One evening Lobojko appeared at the door and was somewhat put out to find that Helena was not in. Gustav was polite but somewhat cold, as he asked the visitor in, and conducted him into the drawing room. There, Gustav's cordiality ceased. In silence he presented Lobojko with a sack of florins, a hundred and fifty, in payment for helping to steer Helena in the right direction. But, with a wave of the hand, Lobojko brushed it aside. Gustav slowly lowered the sack to the table. He was watching those blue eyes of Lobojko. They had darkened with a burning hatred.

There was a touch of triumph in Gustav's voice. "Are you refusing the money, Lobojko?"

The man turned away. His face was pale. His mouth quivered, but he did not speak.

"Because if you are," continued Gustav, "I shall be obliged to terminate your office as my wife's artistic counselor."

He watched Lobojko hesitate, then shrug his shoulders, with a pretense of a smile. "The money is of no importance to me. That is all. But as we are at this moment in the middle of a production, perhaps it is advisable to finish the job."

"And later perhaps something from Shakespeare?" Gustav's irony was quite evident.

"Yes," replied Lobojko, "perhaps something from Shakespeare. And all this at Casino Hall. I trust you have nothing against that."

Gustav was deliberately slow in answering. "I think that will be for Helena to decide . . . for my wife, Helena, to decide. I will have a talk with her." As Lobojko was silent, again, Gustav pressed home his attack. "All these plays that she is studying, I can't think what is to become of them. I am obliged to take Helena with me when I go to Wieliczka. I have some business there concerning the salt mine. From there I must go to Cracow, then possibly to Vienna. You see, my good friend, Helena needs some rest. And after all she is my wife."

Lobojko gave Gustav a quick glance, then, with a gesture that had a touch of mockery about it, he bowed, picked up the bag of money, and left.

As the door closed, Gustav's face lit up with satisfaction. Lobojko was a pest, a scrounger, and a busybody. He, Gustav, had got rid of him with ease. He would be on the lookout for any underhanded moves on Lobojko's part, but now he did not fear the man as before.

Gustav returned to the drawing room and poured himself some wine. Helena would be back in a little while. There would be a lot of questions she would want answered concerning her counselor. She would be expecting Lobojko to wait until she returned from her visit to the local priest, Jawor. His abrupt departure would need explaining. And, of course, Gustav had no intention of taking Helena to Wieliczka or Cracow or any other place in Poland. Bochnia was still the safest spot for Helena.

Sometimes it happens that when man shoots, it is God who takes aim. When Helena came into the room, she found Gustav sprawled in an armchair, somewhat dazed with wine. He sat up, trying to take in what she was saying. The word "Wieliczka" struck him like a thunderbolt. She was going to Wieliczka! Had she met Lobojko, then? No, it was Jawor, the priest. He had asked her to go with him for a few days. It was to help the organization of the home for the workers' children.

"I told him I would go," concluded Helena offhandedly. "We're leaving tomorrow."

Gustav struggled to his feet. "Leaving. . . . You're leaving for Wieliczka . . . leaving—just like that—tomorrow!" He plunged about the room, scratching his bald head, grunting and moaning. He was like some hounded bear of the Carpathian Mountains. But his protests were useless.

"I cannot go back on my promise to the father," she explained, needling him with a touch of irony. "And remember I shall be traveling under the care of an elderly priest, whose housekeeper is quite jealous." Then she began to speak with enthusiasm of the salt mines there, dating back to the thirteenth century, and of the beautiful corridors of salt and the Chapel of St. Anthony. She spoke as if the entire argument had already been settled in her favor.

Gustav pulled himself up and started on a different tack. "It's very strange, Helena, but half an hour ago—perhaps just at the moment you accepted the father's invitation—I was telling Mr. Lobojko that I was planning to take you to Wieliczka and Cracow and possibly Vienna. . . ."

"A mere coincidence!" she broke in. Her voice was flat. "And our intentions were absolutely different."

Gustav felt suddenly depressed and tired. He allowed himself to stretch out on the couch, his arm covering his eyes. He was so much older than Helena, and it weakened his position. She was so willful, so violent and stubborn. Was he losing his control over her? Gustav began to escape in his mind to his own youth, to that time thirty years back—as much as that!—when he visited the Wieliczka mine with the too-youthful Vienna actress, Pauline Poll. The scene was so clear to him—how they went down, twelve hundred feet underground, in a screeching elevator. He remembered that he had told Pauline the story of the Princess Cunegond, whom they called The Blessed.

The Princess was Hungarian and was brought to Cracow by Prince Boleslaw the Modest, as his dearly beloved bride. Before leaving Hungary, the story went, Cunegond paid a farewell visit to the salt-mine workers, and cast about her a handful of gold coins and her royal ring. A few years later in Poland she was approached by a delegation from Cracow. There was great need of salt at a low price. Would she help them to get it from Hungary? Cunegond came down from her throne, and gave orders to all her servants to take up spades and follow her. She walked out of the castle and out of the town, her servants forming a procession behind her. The news spread fast, and as she went the burghers snatched up spades of their own and followed the procession in ever-increasing numbers. Some eight miles from Cracow, near the village of Wieliczka a halt was called by the blessed Cunegond, and she pointed to the ground where they must dig. Almost at once someone dug up a golden ring. It was the one she had cast from her several years before, and in Hungary. Encouraged by this miracle, thousands of burghers, servants, and peasants worked the whole day through without pause, until just as the sun began to go down they came upon their reward—a deposit of salt.

Gustav remembered how Pauline Poll had watched him with large eyes as he told the story, and he remembered how he had been moved to kiss her under the salt statue of the princess in the Chapel of St. Anthony. She had pressed her body against him, and had whispered in pride: "The Hungarian princess discovered the mines. Polish workers are digging them. But your family, Germans, own them."

The words dripped with romanticism. Gustav had been fascinated. And the words had decided the following logical step: a hasty retreat behind the sculptured salt pillars of the Chapel into the dark corridors. . . .

Gustav sat up on the couch, shocked. His dreaming of the past had been shattered by the slamming of the door. One of the paintings in its huge gilt frame squeaked ominously as the wall

felt the tremor. Helena had left the room. Gustav felt stunned,
and alone.

Two days later, Helena departed in the company of Father
Jawor for the salt mines. With them went Mr. Lobojko. The
mines, with galleries and shafts winding for many, many miles,
were filled with legend and mystery. The Chapel of St. Anthony
was the pearl of this underground wonder, totally carved in salt
in the seventeenth century by pious miners down to its most minute detail. On the left as one entered stood the crystal statue
of Cunegond, garbed as a nun with hands clasped in prayer. Opposite her was the patron saint of the miners, St. Barbara, a
torch in one hand, the other resting upon a knight's great sword.
A few steps beyond was an altar, with columns supporting a
high ceiling, which represented the sky. Above this was the cru-
cified Christ flanked by his Mother with a babe in her arms, and
St. Anthony in the robe of a monk, with bowed head, his face
with glistening drops of dew. The odor of dried flowers at the
foot of the Cross, the salt, and the smoke from great oil lamps
mingled and permeated the air, adding to the oppressive sense
of gloom and humidity.

Father Jawor had ceased speaking as they entered the Chapel,
but now he sat down on the narrow steps inviting Helena to sit
beside him, and he continued with his story. From time to time
he glanced up at Lobojko, who stood under the wall, silent and
pale with emotion.

"So as you see, the grandfather of your husband, Wilhelm
Sinnemayer, stole possession of these mines of Wieliczka, not
to mention other vast properties throughout the region. This
Wilhelm stole them from my parents, from the grandfather of
Casimir Lobojko here, and from the Kraszewskis, the Michal-
skis, and the Dolezalis. He stole them through deceit and
through murder. He bribed judges, the courts, the police. He
used the power of the Hapsburgs. He hired crooks and murderers. Yes, even murderers! At their hands Casimir Lobojko's
father met his death."

As Father Jawor paused, he glanced at the beautiful face of
the young girl beside him. It had become as gray as the walls
of the mine. Father Jawor hurried on.

"Now, Wilhelm Sinnemayer's own grandson, Gustav, sells

these properties, bathed in the blood of our forebears, to the bankers of Berlin, Germany. It is your duty, my child, as a wife to stop this transaction. And Casimir Lobojko, here, who loves you dearly, will help you . . . not in theatrical matters alone. . . ."

Father Jawor had turned to Helena. When he saw her face he became silent again. Her eyes were wide and burning with hate; and tears by the light of the lamp were like bright coals on her cheeks. Her mouth was firmly closed as she stood up, her body tense and motionless, like the legendary dragon of Cracow waiting for the time of destruction. Only her eyes moved from the father to Lobojko and back again. Both men watched her in growing alarm, and simultaneously opened their mouths to speak, but their tongues froze in their throats, pierced by the violent eyes of Helena.

The horrible silence was punctured by the steady and slow dropping of water from the ceiling to the stone of the black floor. Helena turned sharply and with steel-cold eyes stared at the figure of Christ, flanked by Mary wth her crown and her babe and St. Anthony with his head bowed in adoration. But Helena's brain was swirling with uncoordinated and violent thoughts, so horrible that not only Christ, but the lowest of sinners, would condemn her. Yet slowly her face, staring up to Christ, became filled with color again. Without warning she turned and ran for the chapel entrance, her wild words crashing against the chapel walls: "I am going to Cracow."

Lobojko, jerked to his senses, ran after her crying out "Helena! Helena! Helena!" with all his might.

Father Jawor rose slowly, adjusted his priestly garb, shook the dust off it, and started down the corridor without haste after the others. When the last syllable of Helena's name rolled along the walls and slid into darkness, the round face of the priest lit up with a slow smile.

9. THE FAITHFUL RETURN

CRACOW, THE eternal city, lay sleeping, yet golden under its crown of rising sun. Because it was not yet five, the only movement in the streets came from the deliverers of bread and the barefoot village women carrying their cans of milk, closely huddled together as they crisscrossed the streets from building to building. Pigeons crowded the sidewalks and gutters, eying the bare feet of the women and the trays of the bread deliverers. With the approach of five o'clock, a movement started among them, first in pairs, then in flocks, flying off as if some sudden news had come to them to head for the Botanical Gardens.

The gardens were bright with the opening buds of flowers, but it was not their intoxicating scent or the fresh green smell of the opening chestnut leaves that attracted the pigeons. They circled a moment above the garden path, known as Chestnut Alley, and descended. Upon a bench sat a young man with black and curly hair, scattering what seemed to be an endless supply of crumbs upon the ground.

Despite the movement of his hand, his thin and pale face seemed sunk in thought. His thick lips and his deep-set black eyes remained unsmiling, even while the pigeons walked without fear over his legs and arms and settled on his head, flapping their wings with a friendly softness. His reaching for crumbs was a slow and deliberate gesture. Each time he let the new store of crumbs slide through his long thin fingers the more courageous birds, jostling for perch upon his narrow shoulders, would slide and flutter down with a melee of beating wings to attack the contents of his hand.

At last the man's pockets were empty and the ground was picked clean. The flocks rose up and scattered over the city, but there remained a few hopeful birds, who were witnesses to something that had never happened to their solitary benefactor in the ten years they had known him. A young and lovely woman came up to the bench and hesitated. As the young man did not seem to be aware of her, she spoke to him. She seemed to be a little embarrassed.

"May I sit down beside you, Igo?"

The deep eyes looked up. The lips opened as if to reply, but no sound came out. The man slowly shook his head. He was staring into the lovely face before him as if he were dreaming, and then he stretched out a halting hand to touch the blue velvet dress. His fingers stroked the pale hand that trembled a little at his touch.

"Yes, it's me, Helena," she murmured. "Only you used to call me Helcia. Do you remember? Are you surprised to see me here? In my school days I used to come here in the summertime and stay here under this chestnut tree to study. . . . It was in the mornings about this time, and with no one to hear me except for the pigeons, I would read Shakespeare aloud, and Schiller. Oh, I remember so well. I—well, after ten years, I wanted to come here again. Does that surprise you?"

As he said nothing, she sat down, but the silence and his searching eyes made her uneasy. She began to speak again, but the childlike quality had gone out of her voice. "And you— what are you doing at this place? I have heard you've become famous, a great portrait painter. And you are part of the night life of the Cracow aristocracy. Surely this should be your time for sleeping. . . ."

The normal color had been flowing back into Igo's face. Now he whispered "Helcia, Helcia!" Then he became silent again, until he turned his eyes from her, and then began to speak with a cold dignity. "It is restful here. That's why I come. I am not at all a great artist. I never was one. But it is true that I am making money now, slapping out portraits of the rich. And I have read about you in the papers—the Cracow papers and the Vienna papers. You are becoming a great actress. Congratulations! Congratulations!"

"Oh stop it!" she cried. "Let's not lie to one another."

Igo did not answer. His face clouded again with sadness. A slight wind stirred the chestnut leaves and the few pigeons flew away, and there was silence. Igo's eyes came up to meet Helena's. Each had longed for this meeting. But now that the miracle had happened, they could find no purpose in it. Helena was married, and had a son and a daughter who bore the name of Modrzejewski. Igo thought about the boy, but he felt he had no right to ask Helena about her family affairs. She may have changed, he thought. It had been so many years. He was afraid to scare her away with the many questions that circled in his mind.

Did she guess his thoughts? She spoke with reproach. "Why didn't you fight for me, Igo? I was young and foolish. I didn't know anything. And there was Mother pushing me into the marriage. But you always had a chance, Igo, if you'd fought for me. Why didn't you convince me? You should've taken me away from Cracow, from my family, from everybody."

He absorbed her words with his eyes and his brain, but the answers stuck like stones in his throat. She was right. It was possible to do almost anything then. But then his power of reasoning was not developed as now. He wondered why she tortured him with these questions. She was no doubt happy now. He would not want to ruin her marriage now. He rose in silence and held his hand toward her, to help her up. A breath of air stirred the leaves of the chestnut again, and a robin began to sing somewhere above their heads.

Arm in arm they strolled out of the gardens into the streets. From time to time their eyes would meet, and there seemed to be a certain fleeting happiness in the silence that existed between them. The people of Cracow were beginning to appear dressed in their Sunday best. Some were window shopping, others buying food at the grocery stores, but most were hurrying to early mass. Carriages were rushing through the streets with drivers shooting their whips above the horses' heads. Peasant carts were rattling along close to the gutter, carts filled with womenfolk wearing brightly colored kerchiefs over their heads. The heavy bells of the Church of the Virgin Mary called them in.

Many of the peasant girls had beautiful, round, happy faces, and their full dresses were the colors of the rainbow. Igo glanced at Helena with a sudden wry smile. "I remember once your mother came to visit us at Krzemionki, and she asked: 'Why is it, that when a Jew wants to marry a Gentile, he picks a woman from the nobility instead of a peasant?' So have a look, Helcia. Look at this cart full of them. Aren't they beautiful?"

"Mother did me so much wrong," sighed Helena as she gazed at the peasant girls going by. "But don't think of my mother. Think of my aunt Theresa who loved me and wanted the best for me. But she would always end with the phrase *"Les mauvaises herbes poussent toujours.'"*

"Yes," said Igo shortly, "I always admired your aunt. She was ahead of her time."

They had been walking for some while before they realized that they were headed for the banks of the Vistula. Igo paused, but Helena spoke quickly. "I want to see our river." He seemed surprised, but took her hand as he had done so long ago and led her down to the meadow, away from the clattering cart wheels and the persistent tolling of bells.

Like some peasant girl after a long and arduous wash day, resting in the meadow grasses, the Vistula quietly breathed in her bed, the scent of wild flowers upon the wind. Her waters were blue, as blue as Helena's dress. Igo kept Helena's hand in his as he led her down the bank, past the willows, past the patch of goldenrod, past the barefooted children fishing with homemade tackle. Igo remembered the years when he too had come here with Helena to fish with homemade tackle in the waters of the Vistula, and he remembered the Sobotkas on St. John's nights—and the last they had spent together.

The river was just as beautiful. The air was filled with the same sweet sense of growing things, but the years. . . . They had gone, although their thoughts tried to recapture the past. Yet peace lay in their hearts for the moment because the day was as pure and innocent as a first love. Rivers, thought Igo, the waters of rivers have often more power than blood to bring people together. They found themselves on the sandy stretch where Igo had beached his boat. Behind them was the meadow and the rising underbrush, and beyond, the city glistening in the morning sun.

Igo was the first to come back to earth. "Let's go back, Helcia. You must be tired."

"Yes," she said, and allowed herself to be led by a short cut back to town. But after a while she broke the silence with a

quick slant of her eyes that reminded Igo of her early days
of flirting. "May I come and see your paintings, Igo? Some-
time after breakfast?"

"Of course. But why not have breakfast with me in my
studio? I moved from Krzemionki, you know. I'm living in
Cracow proper now, at Ulica Grodzka. I only visit my parents
on occasional evenings."

"How are they?" Helena asked graciously, but with little
real interest.

"My father hardly ever goes out on cases. He's too weak
with illness, and he's become old. . . ."

"That's too bad! I always thought your mother was the
weaker one in the family." The remark slipped out without
thinking. As a child Helena had always had a secret hope that
Dr. Neufeld would end by marrying her mother.

Igo looked into her face and smiled. "We are going back—
way back—to childhood. Isn't that right?"

Helena felt herself blushing, but she was annoyed because
she couldn't stop, and she snapped back. "Let's move on to the
city. There's no going back to childhood. It's a thousand times
gone, and the present's irrevocable."

Half an hour later, having hired a fiacre, they came into
the suburbs and reached Ulica Grodzka where Igo had his one-
room studio. It was a huge room, with paintings covering the
walls as in a museum. In the center was a great carved table
with its legs like the paws of a bear. Four chairs stood around
it, in the style made by the mountain folk, their arms carved
in flowers. In one corner of the room was a heavy sofa with
a Lowicki rug above it, and beside it stood an easel with an
unfinished painting of a young woman with an aristocratic
bearing. She had black, burning eyes and a shock of red hair.

The painting was the first object that caught Helena's eye,
and she could not turn away from it. "Who is that woman?"
she asked.

"The Countess Catherine Potocki, Adam's wife."

"She's beautiful, isn't she?"

"She was to come yesterday with her husband. But they
didn't show up."

Helena glanced over the other paintings on the walls. Most

of them were portraits of women, and there were some nude studies, and Helena began to notice a peculiar thing. The faces of all of them, including the Countess Potocki, bore a strange likeness to herself. She glanced at Igo, but he was busy pulling curtains across the windows to keep out the heat of the sun that was pouring in. She sank back onto the sofa with a sigh of fatigue.

"Igo, do you know all your women have something in common? They look like one another."

Igo gave her a guilty look. He looked so much like a small boy caught stealing somebody's apples that she laughed. "It's only an impression," he said lamely. Then, adjusting the last curtain, he added hurriedly, "Rest yourself there a while longer, Helcia. I'll run out and get something to eat for the both of us. There's a restaurant quite near here."

He had rushed out of the room before she could say anything, and she found herself alone with all his painted women. She couldn't just sit there. She wasn't tired any more. Something rose in her that gave her a new strength, and drove her to circle the room. It was like a wave of blood rushing through her body. She was struck with jealousy. All these women, even though they looked so much like her, made her jealous. She went from one to the other, staring with hatred at them all— countesses, princesses, daughters of the rich of Cracow and Vienna. And yet the emotion confused her. Was it the resurrection of that old pure love of so long ago? Or was it something rising out of her life with Gustav? The one thing certain was that Igo still loved her. That was what these paintings said to her. The delicate features, the expression of the lips, the tilt of the nose, or the hair line—there was always something that recalled *her*. Obviously, although perhaps not always consciously, Igo never failed to return to Helena for his love fulfillment.

The passing of time began to be unbearable to Helena as she stalked the room like some caged animal. She persisted in lifting her hands to her head until her hair was in disorder, and the sudden thought struck her, as if it had no relation to herself, that she was instinctively letting her braids come down. Her fingers clutched at the gold buttons on her blouse. Her poor breasts were there, pressed together by the high wall of corset. On reaching the sofa again, she stopped and began to undress. Her heart pounded violently, and her fingers were possessed with a frantic desire for speed, and she stepped away from her fallen pleated skirt and pulled at her underwear, frantic to find release from its tight embrace.

In freeing herself of all her clothing, she felt she was like a flower opening to the sun. She ran her hands down her thighs, and straightened her long legs to stand on her toes and stretch, but she suddenly broke into tears, and crumpled onto the sofa.

Igo came in, loaded with packages, and was about to place them on the table, when he stood entranced by what he saw. Like that—stripped of the sophistication of her dress—she looked still so young, as he remembered her, wanted her. Throwing the packages down, he rushed to her side, falling on his knees, his lips feeling the burning of her flesh, his hands gathering her to him, sensing the suppleness of her eager willing body. . . .

It was well advanced into the afternoon before Helena and Igo sat down to their belated breakfast. Helena was dressed and radiant now, a light in her eyes that Igo worshipped. They had forgotten the world, and all responsibility to it, and were quite stunned by a sudden knock on the door.

Igo recovered quickly, and laughed. He got up. "That's just the janitor, darling. He cleans the studio Sunday afternoons, the time I visit my parents in Krzemionki."

He opened the door briskly and started to speak, but stopped. He was mistaken. In the doorway stood Count Adam Potocki with his wife Catherine, who was dressed in white and wore a flowered hat.

"Perhaps I am intruding," said the Count, observing Igo's hesitation. "I have come with my wife to see the portrait, for she cannot stop talking about it."

Igo backed away slightly. "You may see it, of course." He glanced back at Helena, and she saw that his face was a picture of confusion. "But first, please allow me to present . . ."

"Not at all," interrupted the Count. "We already know each other quite well. That was before she left Cracow, of course.

Then she played in the theatres of Cracow. And more recently I have seen her in her stage triumphs at Lwow."

Helena rose and smiled. The Count bowed over her hand, then turned to his wife. "This is the famous actress Helena Modrzejewska. And you may judge for yourself how truly beautiful she is."

The women nodded politely, but the Count seemed explosively happy as he carried on a stream of conversation. "Once I was in love with Madame, and my fond mother even wanted me to ask for your hand. But I am afraid Pan Sinnemayer got there before me. And by the way, why did Madame change her name to Modrzejewska?"

"Adam," murmured the Countess in distress, "is it not too many questions and too much reminiscing for the first meeting?"

Igo had recovered himself sufficiently to close the door. He moved forward quickly. "Won't you please sit down, and reminiscing will come that much easier."

Helena seated herself with self-conscious grace in a chair. "I don't think we have very much to remember."

"Ah, but yes!" protested the Count. "Helena Modrzejewska, the symbol of beauty, the epitome of talent, and I . . ."

Helena smiled and finished the sentence for him: "And you, Count Potocki, symbol of European aristocracy and wealth. . . ."

"Each to his own," interjected the Countess, eying her former rival.

The Count glanced at her a little bleakly, but she hurried on. "We are giving a reception tonight for Fritz Devrient, the famous Vienna actor, you know. Would you honor us with your presence, Madame Modrzejewska? The cream of the European stage will be there. May we expect you, and . . . and your husband?"

"I thank you," said Helena, "but my husband is not here. I came to Mr. Neufeld to talk over the possibility of his doing a portrait of my husband. . . ."

"Please come," said the Countess simply, and her eyes strayed to her husband's face. "It would be so nice for you and Mr. Devrient to meet." She turned to Igo. "And you, Mr. Neufeld, will of course come. You must. . . ."

Igo took his cue, and began by addressing Helena. "I most
certainly will paint the portrait of your husband, Madame. And
I'll do it in a much shorter time than I took to paint Countess
Potocki's. There is so much less beauty to capture in a man,
you see. But so it will be, and Madame Modrzejewska most
assuredly may accept the invitation, if I may be allowed to
escort her. . . ."
Helena smilingly nodded her head in acceptance.

The reception at the Potocki Palace was composed of about
one hundred and fifty guests, including the leading artists from
Cracow, Vienna, Warsaw, and Berlin. A twenty-piece orchestra
played Viennese waltzes, Polish polonaises, and French quad-
rilles in the vast Crystal Hall, paneled with mirrors and lit by
four huge chandeliers. In the side halls exquisite French wines
were drowning the Polish hams, the roasted turkeys and pheas-
ants.

Most conspicuous among the guests was the distinguished
figure of Devrient, and the eyes of everyone turned frequently
to the sight of him standing at the entrance of one of the side
rooms off the main hall, deeply immersed in a conversation with
Igo Neufeld and Helena Modrzejewska. They were speaking of
methods in producing Shakespeare's plays for the European
stage. "The Great Fritz," as he was known in the theatrical
circles, was enchanted with Helena's beauty and her deep knowledge of classical repertory. Igo was quick to see this and to
maneuver the conversation around until he succeeded in getting
from the actor an invitation for Helena to come to Vienna and
play in his theatre.

Those who knew Devrient personally swore that he never
made rash promises, that a beautiful woman, if she had no talent, would never attract his attention, and that he had a keen
appreciation of young and unusual talent.

It was past midnight when Helena and Igo left the Potocki
Palace. Cracow was asleep. The streets glistened with rain, and
from the palace gardens came the heavy scent of flowers in full
bloom. Helena was happy, and leaning on Igo's arm, she held
him back from walking too fast, as if she wanted to prolong the
evening indefinitely.

10. MARYLKA

A WARM southern breeze blew down from the Carpathian Mountains upon the Rumanian town of Cernauti. The peasant houses dozed in the glaring sun, and below them roared the River Pruth, drowning overripe chestnuts and cherries as the wind rolled them to the brink. Hardened by battles with Turkish and Russian invaders and with the native oppressors of the Hohenzollern-Sigmazingen family, the Rumanian patriots could still boast to each newcomer: "Look at our country. Only Rumanian trees can blossom so richly in the spring, and smell so sweet and strong. And just wait until the tobacco plants and the sunflowers and the corn bloom, and you will never want to leave Rumania." While others would add: "Even the cows smell better here. Look at them there against the green fields and the golden flowers. Why, they even chew the grass differently."

Rumanians are talkative and very convincing. And in this case truth was on their side. It was enough only to glance from the top floor of the Hotel Alba Julia, at the town below and at the sunlit countryside around it, to be convinced.

Helena stood before the open window on the top floor gazing into the far distance. The scent of fresh flowers flowed up to her at every gust of wind, but she was hardly aware of anything. She was alone and deeply immersed in her thoughts, and she frowned without realizing it. Her six-month-old daughter Marylka lay contentedly in her crib in the adjoining room. Rudolph, who was now four, had gone for a walk with his nurse.

Helena had written long ago to her mother and her half-brother Felix in Cracow, asking them to come to Cernauti. She could not continue this way, leaving her children to the care of servants, while she ran a household and carried on a full stage career at the same time. Some solution had to be found to her problems first. Perhaps her family could help. But they were a long time in coming, and the days passed slowly, stretching out to eternity.

97

One thing was certain. It had been three years since she had
fled Gustav, and nothing would induce her to return to him,
neither his pleadings, nor his promises, nor his threats, nor the
risk of suffering the most dire consequences. All illusion was at
an end. There was no retreat. She could not forget the words
of Father Jawor in the salt mines of Wieliczka. She had even
investigated and verified the facts. The business affairs of Gustav and his family had become to her like an evil monster, as
pernicious as a Cracowian dragon, which spattered its poison
everywhere. It infected anything that might have existed between them. Father Jawor was right. How could a man so cruel
and heartless in his business love his home and his wife with
the devotion he claimed? Helena could not imagine him capable
of loving anyone but himself and his wealth. What was a beautiful wife to him but a means for expanding his egotism? She
fed the pride of a man who was impotent, and she was the excuse for his acquiring new wealth.

Helena could feel no guilt in deserting him. She owed him
no gratitude for her theatrical success in Cracow, Lwow, Poznan, Warsaw, Vienna, Cernauti. He had not helped her. With
his crooked dealings he only hindered her. "Such is my destiny,"
thought Helena, "to go through life alone. . . ."

She walked away from the window and into her daughter's
room. A sudden sense of loneliness made her pick the baby up
and press her close. She caressed her with all the tenderness that
only a mother can feel. The little girl's round pink face creased
in a smile, and Helena stepped over to the open window to show
Marylka the colors of Rumania's spring.

There was a knock on the door. It would be Rudolph with his
nurse, or perhaps her mother and Felix. She went to open the
door, and then stood motionless. Gustav was standing before
her.

"When a wife fails to come to her husband, the husband
comes to his wife, whom he loves. May I come in?"

She nodded briefly, and hastily turned back to the living room,
holding her daughter tight in her arms. Gustav followed. His
obese body seemed to stagger as he made his way to the nearest
armchair, throwing aside his black cape and hat. He sprawled

in the chair, and to create a breeze waved his arms about like
oars.

"I'm out of breath. May I have some water?"

Helena glanced in the direction of the kitchen and then at the
child in her arms.

"I'll hold her," he said. "Give her to me."

She placed the baby in the big coarse hands of her husband,
and then stared fearfully at what she had done.

"What's its name?"

"Marylka," she said, as she hurried to the kitchen. She was
clumsy in her haste to return to the child again. She had a glass
of water on a tray, and was starting back, when she heard
something that made her run. "What happened?" she cried.

"I don't know," said Gustav above the child's screaming.
"She started to cry." He seemed embarrassed and was sweating
profusely. "Maybe she's hungry."

Helena set the tray on a table and took the baby. Gustav
looked from the child's face to Helena's. He seemed to compare
their beauty. But he said nothing. The beads of perspiration on
his face increased. He smiled ironically.

Helena took the crying child to the bedroom and set her on
the bed. The door of the room was ajar so that Gustav could
see part of Helena's worried profile as she sat on the bed com-
forting her daughter. The light curtains blew in behind her as
the wind slipped in off the fruit trees, and the scent of blossoms
filled the room. Helena's hair looked copper-red against the light.
Yet the full effects of spring could not soothe Gustav's bitter
heart. His voice came to her flat and morose.

"The same father?"

She jerked up her head like a high-strung horse, and answered
him in short, violent sentences. "That's not your business. Certainly not yours. I want to have children. Why did you come
here? We're finished."

There was silence. Gustav did not answer at once. He chose
his words. He weighed all the arguments. He raised the glass of
water to his lips and gulped it down. Then he got to his feet, his
hand still grasping the back of the chair.

"Let me talk. I want two minutes. After two minutes I'll
leave, if you still want that. Do you hear me?"

"As you wish," she said. She placed the child in the crib. There was a quiet strength about her as she came into the room, closing the bedroom door behind her. It made Gustav angry, because of his helplessness.

She looked at him scornfully. "Before you begin with your explanations I should warn you that I know all there is to know about your family . . . everything . . . all that you tried to keep from me by lying. All the sins that I have committed you know from me, not from someone else. And anyway mine don't hurt anyone but myself. I didn't cause anyone's death. I didn't make a fortune through anyone else's sufferings . . . but you, Gustav —through blood of others and tears. . . . And even for those few sins I have committed you are partly to blame. . . . You shouldn't have married me at your age . . . steeping me in promises you never kept . . . cheating me. . . ."

"Woman—it's enough!" Gustav's anger thundered her into silence. "*You* talk—you who go around like an animal—a beast —bearing young each time from someone else. Is that my fault, too, then? And you, your position in the theatre that you're so proud of now—that came from my pockets. Thanks to my position and my efforts. Don't you forget that."

Helena chose a chair near the window. It was as far away from him as possible. There was no softening in her voice, though she spoke without forcing. "You're lying, of course. All lies. Bochnia—that miserable little town—it would have been my grave if I hadn't had the strength to pull out. As for my getting on the stage in Poland and Vienna, you had nothing to do with that. I work hard, that's why, and I can act better than others. I am climbing up to the top, and I don't need any of your kind of help, your underhanded manipulations and swindles. . . . I don't want you with me, or with my children. I don't want any part of you. So there's nothing for you to do but go."

He was silent for a moment, staring at her, his breath coming in short gasps, as if he were trying to control his rage. Then he spoke haltingly, "Do you remember on the road to Bochnia . . . the first time . . . we stopped at that inn. . . . Then . . . they broke right into the room . . . and tried to kill me. Remember that, Helena. It was Igo Neufeld who tried to kill me . . . your Igo. . . ."

Helena clutched the chair, her face paling. "You're mad!"

But Gustav took a step nearer and held up a hand, the five fingers spread out in his urgency. "Wait, wait. . . . What I want to say is—it may seem strange—in spite of it, in spite of that —my love for you is as burning as ever. . . ."

She ignored his love. "So he wanted to kill you—that's what you say. If that's true, then why did I save you? . . . Do you remember that . . . the scalding tea that I threw in the face of one of them. You're mad!"

"Yes, Helena. That's what *you* did. That's why I love you. I want you to come back to me, to Bochnia. Look—forget the theatre, forget everything that has come between us. I'm ready to forget, to forgive . . . your past mistakes, this foolishness about the theatre that destroys the home, all the security in life. I've come here to ask you, Helena—come back, and there'll be nothing between us."

"Gustav," she cried, "you don't believe your own words." She rose from the chair and faced him, her implacable eyes burning into him. "You yourself don't believe that Igo would be capable of such a thing. It was done by the people of Bochnia. You know that. They hate you, Gustav. They didn't want you there, selling all they could scrape together to the Berlin banks. Why should these people have to greet you with a triumphal procession, you who are to them the symbol of Prussian swindling? No—what they wanted was a funeral procession into Bochnia, with you in the coffin. That's why they tried to kill you. I know now."

Gustav stood motionless, in the middle of the room, his arms hanging at his sides, his palms open. The pale waxen face stiffened, and the perspiration came down his cheeks like tears.

Helena moved closer to him. "Leave me, Gustav. I don't want to be near you any more, or to listen to you. Go and give your secrets to someone else. . . ."

Gustav did not reply. He turned and mechanically reached for his cape and hat. He walked out, without looking back, wiping his bald head with his red hand. Helena stood motionless, staring after him, when she became suddenly conscious that her child was crying at the top of her lungs. She hurried into the bedroom, plucked Marylka off the bed, and rocked her back and

forth. But it was all useless. Beating her small arms in the air,
like a newborn bird fallen out of the nest with helpless wings,
Marylka went on crying. The distraught mother rocked her
daughter in her arms, cuddled her, walking around the room.
She tried to talk to the child, pleaded, sang, cried. But nothing
helped. An hour passed. The rending cries of little Marylka continued, and even grew in strength. In fear, Helena ran out into
the hall and called for help.

Within fifteen minutes, a Dr. Tatarescu arrived. Helena trembled in the grip of some terror caused by an intuition, inexpres-
sible. The doctor shook his head and gave her several spoons of
a white powder dissolved in water. Gradually the screams began
to diminish, and little Marylka closed her eyes, breathing heavily
—as before a sudden death, thought Helena.

"What did Madame feed her child?" asked the doctor frowning.

"The breast."

The frown vanished. "Oh, then everything will be all right.
If it had nothing but milk from the breast, the child will be fine
by tomorrow." Dr. Tatarescu showed his yellowing teeth and
bowed low. "I admire Madame's acting on the stage. Great skill.
Great skill." Then he left, and the hotel maids followed him.

Once again alone with her child, Helena kneeled beside the
crib and prayed aloud. Her face became serene and her color returned. Her eyes shone with drying tears and in their place came
hope. It brightened her whole face, so classic in its strong beauty,
framed by the copper of her hair. And her voice took on a more
dramatic quality, as her prayer led her to her own problems, and
away from the child she thought already well. She spoke with
God as rarely two people speak, sincerely, honestly, from her
heart. She did not complain and she did not plead. For the first
time in her life, Helena discarded her willfulness, seeking advice
and help beyond herself.

But often the ways of God seem strange to man. That same
evening at eleven o'clock, April 28, 1865, Helena's little daughter died. Brokenhearted, the mother accepted the fate of her child
with a deep sense of humility. Death is the ruthless dictator of
existence. The death of the innocent is always repaid, because a
wrong forever remains in the memory of God and man.

11. THE NEXT STEP

IT WAS Madame Opid's opinion that Gustav was an ideal husband for her daughter. She continued to maintain this view despite the latest trouble. Gustav was devoted. He was clever. He was rich. What more could a girl want? And what could be more desirable for the entire family?

Now Helena was calling her to Cernauti. Very well. She would stop at Bochnia on her way and speak to Gustav. She would find out just what his future plans were. Gustav had always been kind and considerate toward her. He would surely listen to counsel from her, and furthermore be pleased to find her on his side. Then she would move on to Cernauti and take her willful child in hand. Her son Felix would go along with her. Felix might even be of help. He had become an actor before Helena went on the stage and had won some attention in his own right. Helena should be glad to see him, and perhaps to listen to him on the matter of Gustav.

Madame Opid's careful planning for her trip delayed her considerably, and it was her undoing. She arrived in Bochnia to find all the townspeople indulging in a magnificent funeral arranged by Father Jawor. In its mood and its colorfulness, it seemed more like a festival out in the fields than a funeral, except that there was no dancing. Two men had died and died mysteriously—some said in the salt mines, some that they were killed in a brawl, others that they both committed suicide. Whatever the real cause, Madame Opid's shock was complete. The buried men were Gustav and Casimir Lobojko. They had both been a riddle to many during their lives. They both remained an enigma now they were dead.

Madame Opid had no time to inquire deeply into the details of her son-in-law's death. It sufficed for her that he was dead, and that Helena would have to take up a new life from this point on. She was considerably put out, however, to find that Gustav's financial affairs were so tangled that it would be necessary to hire lawyers from Cracow and Vienna to unravel them. No testament or written statement of any kind could be found in his house. Madame Opid, in a distraught state of mind, was forced to hurry to Cernauti. And at Cernauti a new tragedy awaited her. At the Hotel Alba Julia, they informed her that her daughter had left the city with her four-year-old son, and mourning the sudden loss of her little Marylka by some inexplicable ailment.

Madame Opid stood at the desk transfixed with horror, and for once had nothing to say. It was Felix who asked the manager if he knew where Helena had gone. But the man shook his head and produced two letters addressed to Madame Modrzejewska, both from theatrical managements, one from Vienna and the other from Budapest. Probably invitations to make an appearance in these centers. Madame was always getting such letters. But what could he do with these? Both had arrived after she had left.

Madame Opid took the letters with her and climbed back into the carriage. Felix for the first time thought how tired she looked. There was nothing to do but return to Cracow.

"He who cries in his youth will rejoice and laugh in later years," quoted Felix in his best theatrical voice, trying to rouse his mother out of her misery. "Look at these letters, Mama— from Vienna, from Budapest! What more could an actress demand than such fame?"

Madame Opid reached for the letters. She wanted to convince herself of the reality of these theatre offers. She glanced at Felix.

He laughed. "Open them—of course. Helena won't care."

Both letters said the same thing. Helena was eagerly awaited. The whole theatrical season was hers at a fat salary.

"You see," cried Felix, "Helena won't give up. She can become rich and famous without Gustav. Anyhow that old goat only got in her way."

"Oh, but what are you talking about! She loved Gustav!"

Felix was pleased to see his mother rising to the bait, and spurred her a little more. "She loved Marylka, and she loves Rudolph, yes, but when you talk about Gustav—that's different. You don't know Helena, Mama."

"I don't know her? Don't be childish, Felix. She's my daughter. In flesh and blood the same woman as I." Madame Opid, thoroughly roused, was fast forgetting her own dismay. "I tell you, Helena knows her worth. And she's not conceited either. She's a real person. She has a great talent for acting, and that's where all her troubles begin." Then she added as an after-thought, quite unmindful of the fact that she was now agreeing with Felix on the matter. "Of course, she has to put away all the unhappy things of the past and look ahead. She's young, and she has a whole fascinating life ahead of her. But you forget, Felix, or perhaps you are too young to understand, before she forgets she must suffer, like the Greek tragediennes suffered. But this time there is no stage. It is real—her own life."

"But you've got to help, Mama. It's only you who can get her back to normal again. The tragedy would be if a woman like Helena were to waste any time at all mourning a man like Gustav."

"You know, Felix, I've done a lot for her," cried his mother, "and I'll do more now to help her get on the right path." She finished with a meaningful glance at her son, "Anyhow, I already have plans for her. . . ."

Felix smiled understandingly. His mother was on the right path again, anyway.

Madame Opid became silent, listening to the monotonous creaking of the carriage, until she dozed off into sleep.

That same day, several hours after Madame Opid and her son Felix had returned to the family home at 7 Szeroka Street, Cracow, another carriage drew up at the door, and Helena got out, helping Rudolph down with exaggerated care. She was quiet, her face pale, her eyes red, and so deep was she with res-ignation, that even her mother moved softly about her with as few words as she was capable of limiting herself to. It turned out that Helena had not heard of the death of Gustav, but she accepted the news with barely a comment, other than a subdued reference to God's will, and mention of the fact that she would retain her husband's name for the stage. She put Rudolph to bed and immediately herself fell into a deep, exhausted sleep.

"That only shows how honest she is," Felix mused out loud, thinking of the retention of Gustav's name. "Besides, that wasn't Gustav's real name. He only took it because Helena insisted. You

see, Mama, Helena proves her uprightness by keeping for hers
the name of an unfortunate marriage. She will remember Gustav
Modrzejewski."

Madame Opid, however, did not concern herself with such
minor details. Her hands were quite full enough, for her plan
had to be turned into action. First she furnished for Helena a
modest but comfortable apartment on the second floor of the
house that had been rebuilt after the great fire. She took charge
of little Rudolph as often as possible so that Helena might rest
and have no cares during the period before she returned to her
theatrical career. In fact, Madame Opid's whole attitude toward
her daughter seemed to have changed. She had learned her lesson in regard to Helena. That girl could not be forced into anything. She must deal with her with great subtlety. Helena was
being treated as though she were mistress of the house, and
made all the decisions. All suggestions and ideas apparently came
from outside. Helena was without suspicion that her mother still
had her crafty fingers in the pie.

A young American actor, Maurice Neville, came to Cracow.
He put on *Hamlet,* which he played in English although the rest
of the cast played in Polish. It occurred to Madame Opid to ask
Mr. Neville to substitute *Mary Stuart* for his fall production
with Helena as the lead. For this she needed help. She went to
see Count Adam Potocki. She knew that the Count had for a
long time nourished a deep feeling for her daughter, and it was
well known that his fortune and his influence could get him anything he wished with the mere flick of an eyelash.

Several days passed. Then Helena received a written invitation from the Count to a ball at his palace, where she would meet
the actor Maurice Neville. Madame Opid pretended great surprise when Helena showed her the note, and made no effort to
persuade her daughter to go. It was quite on her own that Helena decided, and asked her brother Felix to escort her.

The Count, for his part, had already worked on Neville, praising Helena's acting beyond measure. But it was unnecessary.
After several minutes of conversation with Helena, he recognized the inner powers of this lovely girl. There were many dazzling beauties at the Count's ball that night, but Maurice Neville
never once left Helena's side. He spoke of her as material for

a great artist. He discussed with her and the Count the classical repertoire and the possibilities of acting in America.

That evening at the Potocki Palace ball, surrounded by the glittering splendor of European aristocracy, the future was decided for Helena. Many, many years after the event, the distinguished Polish actor, Ludwik Solski, who starred with Helena on the Cracow stage, could write these words with deep sincerity:

What a splendid woman she was! Not only beautiful, not only full of graciousness and peace, but also straightforward and simple. Her audiences were stirred to the depth by her. In all my stage experience, I have never seen other actresses who can compare with her. A genius was hidden in this woman. She was great in comedy and as great in straight drama. Her Viola—ah, sheer poetry! Lady Macbeth—exciting! But her most powerful role was Mary Stuart. People trembled in the audience and behind the scenes. Her voice was of tremendous range—from a whisper that dripped with emotion to a magnificent and awful power. . . . Ah, one had to see her!

A sincere friendship grew up between us from the time of the production of *Much Ado About Nothing,* when she played Beatrice, and I Dogberry. When I came onto the stage she burst out laughing and turned away from the audience. It set the audience to roaring, and I was acutely embarrassed. But after the performance she sent a note to my dressing room, which read: "You will be marked for the perpetual laughter of success which I experienced seeing you in your role." From that time on, Modrzejewska gave me stature before the Cracow audiences by her words: "Here you have a young actor who can be put into any Shakespearean role, including the female characters."

But it's true that all others felt themselves insignificant beside her. Exceptionally lovely, intelligent. In perfect command of several languages. Dominating any situation both on the stage or off it.

12. QUAND-MÊME

IT SEEMS that no matter from what height it falls a cat can always land on its four paws, straighten itself out and march off unabashed. And people are often like cats in this way. It happened to Helena Modrzejewska at this time, so young to be widowed and mourning the loss of a child. Yet with her success at the Cracow Theatre, she was able to shake off her stupor, all sense of despair, and plunge into work. The more she worked the more vitality she expressed. The past went into oblivion while she gained an inspiring sense of life.

Being of a religious turn of mind, she had an almost mystic love of her country and its people. And since her investigation into her husband's affairs, she had become most ardently patriotic in her resentment of foreign domination.

Politically, economically, and culturally, the Polish nation was far from backward, and the enslavement by her three powerful neighbors—Austria, Germany, and Russia—since 1772 was cause for much bitterness and restlessness. As it was, the Austrians ruled in Cracow, the Germans in Poznan, and the Russians in Warsaw, and all by agreement with each other so that bondage for Poland was complete. Again and again the people rushed to arms in an effort to shake off the foreign yoke. The last of these insurrections, that of 1863, plunged the nation into such a sea of blood that no one could feel unscathed.

The hero patriots of the insurrection were practically worshipped as saints. Many of them were women, such as the famous Jadwiga Wolska, Wiktoria Jankiewicz, and Henryka Pustowojt. To Helena these fearless women were models of greatness.

The tragic result of these rebellions was the slow destruction of the flower of Polish youth. Still more tragically, there was that vast class of people, the peasant and worker of Poland, who had never known any life but subjection and could not be expected to see that freedom for them could never begin while

Poland was a mere system of colonies exploited by foreigners. Culture must first be made to grow in Poland and with it the building of a higher economic status. So argued the politically enlightened among the Poles. The main aim was to build a vast potential force that at the proper moment would concertedly rise to arms, and by the sheer force of a popular movement drive out the oppressive foreign rulers and establish Poland's independence and a more democratic concept of government.

New factories and new business enterprises were organized in all parts of the country—in Warsaw, Lodz, Katowice, in cities, in towns, throughout the country. It was done by encouraging French, British, and native investors, who would build up the economy of the land for the sake of a good profit to themselves. The Polish workers found work; many Polish peasants migrated willingly from their exhausted farmlands to the centers of industry, becoming industrial workers. A large part of the peasantry returned home from their desperate search for work in Austria, Germany, and Russia and went to work in Polish factories.

Konrad Proszynski set a healthy precedent by organizing "Circles of Education" in the working-class centers, where, free of charge, the Polish workers could learn more about their own language, their own history, and its slow growth toward enlightenment. These were overtly cultural undertakings to keep the people out of trouble, but under cover it meant the spread of Polish patriotism.

Helena was stirred deeply by these endeavors. She herself could make use of the theatre for educational purposes, despite stern persecution by foreign censorship. She loved to work. She loved to feel that Poland was a place of vital youth, marching to a great future. Her energies seemed boundless. She would accept opera engagements to sing mezzo-soprano roles. She would sing in operettas. She would appear on the stage in plays of high value, yet seemed always just as willing to accept an invitation to play in vaudeville. Then she was particularly fond of giving an evening recital. She would read the Polish national poets from Jan Kochanowski to Juliusz Slowacki and Adam Mickiewicz, who in his most famous *Ode to Youth* appealed to them:

Together young friends!
Happiness for all is everyone's goal.

The theatres of Cracow, Poznan, and Warsaw were soon to
revolve around Helena as their great star, and with the money
she earned she financed touring companies in which she played
without being paid. She traveled from city to city, from village
to village. Neither the censors nor the police could cope with
her. She disarmed them with her beauty and her gracious smile.
Or when either seemed slow to work, she would bribe them,
thereby getting permission to stage as yet uncensored plays and
comedies ridiculing the foreign rulers. It served to fortify the
morale and national spirit of those who constituted eighty per-
cent of the nation—the long-exploited peasants and laborers.

The classic repertoire of the nation was the most successful—
the popular *Dziady* by Adam Mickiewicz, and Juliusz Slowacki's
Lilla Weneda, Balladyna, and *Anhelli.* This last, a narrative
dramatized for the stage, portrayed the sufferings of the Poles
in Siberia. Then there was the stirring, hard-hitting *Undivine
Comedy* by the great poet of the romantic school, Zygmunt Kra-
sinski. It showed the triumph of the pure ideal over materialism
and oppression, and rose to a climax when one of the heroes
shouts with his dying breath, "Galilean, the victory is yours!"

The number of Polish dramas produced by Helena Modrzejewska at this time is legion. She played parts in them all, and
should one of the actors fall ill before curtain time she would
take over the male role and play it like a man. Her voice range
was a constant source of astonishment.

In some sectors occupied by the Russians or the Germans, the
censorship was so strict that it was impossible to present a Polish
play. Very well—Helena appeared in Molière, Schiller, Shakespeare. Still by the use of subtle emphasis and pantomine she
would succeed in introducing a thoroughly patriotic note, and
accentuating the triumph of good over evil. The authorities were
unable to protest even while it was quite obvious the audience
had not missed her intent. The local safety authorities were in
a funk as soon as this "actress of everything" appeared on the
scenes with her touring company. They never knew whether
her performances might not end in hostile manifestations

against the administration either in the theatre or in the streets
of the town.

In the summer of 1866, Helena visited Poznan, which at that
time was going through a period of sharpened persecution by
the German police. In the middle of the night people would be
dragged out of their beds and deported into the far interior of
Germany to work on the land or be put into the army. For this
location, Helena carefully chose the plays of Shakespeare. As
her first offering, it was announced, she would appear as Lady
Macbeth. The arrival of Helen Modrzejewska from Cracow
caused a stir throughout the district, and on opening night the
theatre was packed dangerously beyond its capacity. Where the
people could not sit, they stood, pressed against each other,
shoulder to shoulder, without complaint. In fact, they became so
quickly absorbed in the acting that they made no sound. This
rapt intensity of the audience had an electrifying effect on the
actors. Helena herself was never in better form.

The authorities grew increasingly nervous. The German
police, in uniform and in plainclothes, formed a cordon around
the theatre, blocking all the exits. Crowds had assembled outside, hoping for a glimpse of the famous actress. Something
was bound to happen in all that tense excitement. No one knew
how it began, but as the final curtain came down over a thousand people rose to their feet and burst into the national anthem
of Poland.

> Jeszcze Polska nie zginela,
> Kiedy my zyjemy.
> Co nam obca przemoc wziela,
> Szabla odbierzemy. . . .

Some excited youths rushed onto the stage, lifted Helena to
their shoulders, and carried her, still dressed in the majesty of
Lady Macbeth, up through the audience and toward one of the
exits. And the cheers through the house were deafening. The
mass of people outside had heard the singing of the Polish
anthem, and were moved to demonstrate their patriotic feeling,
over five thousand strong. The police tried vainly to restore
some sort of order, but the crowds were increasing and acquired
a sudden menacing aspect. The police called on the army for

help. The people were arming themselves with sticks, shovels, and frames they had broken from the windows. Explosion was imminent.

Out into this scene of seething tension came Helena borne aloft, like the symbol and rallying point for revolt. For a moment the authorities seemed stunned by the spectacle. In that moment, Helena began to struggle and cry out to be set down. The next moment the arms of foreign law began to converge in her direction. They would arrest her and clap her in jail, and as everyone knew it was not so easy to get out of a German jail. Between her and confinement was the jostling mob of excited people, and the course of the law was slowed long enough for Helena to slide to the ground and melt into the human mass.

She pushed and shoved and plunged her way through to the fringes of the crowd, and off into the outer darkness without once glancing back to see if she were being followed. She ran down the narrow, echoing, empty streets with only the moon on the cobblestones to light her way. She gasped for breath, and slowed her pace. She had become aware of the blindness of her running. The shock was wearing off. She stopped and listened, only to start at the clatter of fast approaching footsteps. She clutched at her long dress and started on again, but her breath was coming heavily. She knew that her strength was waning.

"Come what may," she choked, "I can't run any more." And she collapsed on the semicircular steps of the nearest building. She wiped the perspiration from her forehead with the hem of her gown. Her body seemed to shake with her quick breathing and the pounding of her pulse. Out of the darkness appeared the thin, dark form of a man. He turned his face to her so that the moon caught his smile, and she stared up at him in astonishment. Was this the one who had been pursuing her? He was young and blonde with curly hair. In fact he looked little above twenty. And he was obviously very well dressed.

"But you run . . . how you run . . . like a deer from the forests of Bialowieza," he said, and he was clearly very much out of breath. "Madame, I am a Pole, like yourself. I am no policeman, nor any other kind of agent. My name is Tadeusz Nietzsche. I want to help you."

There was something about the simple candor of the young

man that appealed to Helena, but she felt it wise to be on her dignity, after all that ignominious running. "I don't need any help, thank you. I shall wait here for a while. I was just resting. I will call a fiacre."

The young man gazed solemnly at her. "It won't be as easy as you seem to think. The streets are empty, don't you see? And if you decide to walk, the police will spot you at once in that costume."

His voice and manner were verging on the pompous, she thought. She would make things difficult for him. "Then I shall stay here." And she arranged her gown as if making herself comfortable for a long stay.

The young man stared at her even more intently. "Here? On these steps?"

"It's very comfortable here." The thought of moving really made her feel faint at the moment.

The young man's eyes moved upward to the building behind her. He spoke loud and clear, as though he were giving a lecture on architecture to a large audience. "One of the most ancient and surely one of the most beautiful of Polish creations. I assure you, Madame, if we were in more favorable circumstances, I would be delighted to tell you the history of this building. But how can I expose you to such danger? The Germans have taken over this house of tradition. This, Madame, is the very seat—I will not say 'heart'—of the German administration. To be frank this is the City Hall."

"Oh!" She looked back at the building, uncertainly.

The young man's voice went on with almost monotonous precision. "The disturbance you set off at the theatre has apparently emptied the nest. But, like hornets, they will return, Madame. You can see for yourself, that that is inevitable. They will further be frustrated and irritable. They will seize you at once, and take you in there for investigation. Should I say a grilling? For this reason. . . ."

"For this reason," interrupted Helena, jumping up, "let's hide in the darkness of the arcades over there."

"Yes, yes. That is a very wise suggestion."

As she stepped down, he offered her his arm, but Helena merely laughed and ran off in front of him. She crossed a few semicircular steps and found herself under the arcades that seemed to her to be in the style of the Renaissance. She sat down on a bench that was just out of the halflight of the street lamp. She looked up and smiled as the young man appeared, slim and black against the light.

"You cannot stay here very long, Madame," he said. "It is necessary for you to hide from the police while you are at Poznan. If you will allow me to be your protector, I should be pleased to obtain some clothes from my sister. I will procure a friend's coach and we will find a safe place for you to stay for a few days."

"Please sit down," she said sweetly, but he seemed to hesitate, and she added, "Don't feel embarrassed by Lady Macbeth. She's been through so much already. She's committed many crimes, don't forget, and is surely able to look after herself quite well."

Young Tadeusz sat down stiffly beside her. She looked at the outline of his profile and got the impression that he felt he was being made fun of. She pulled her gown around her. It was now ripped in several places. She spoke quietly with great seriousness, and her low notes thrilled him. "I'm really very much intrigued with all this protection you are offering me."

Instead of giving her a direct answer, he began to talk in his curiously stiff voice which pronounced each word emphatically, as if he intended to prolong his conversation with the famous actress as long as possible. "We inhabitants of Poznan are proud of our City Hall. It goes back to the thirteenth century, and was enlarged in the sixteenth century. On a fine day, when the light of the sun strikes against the arcades and the ornamental facade—how lovely it is! You have no idea, Madame. . . ."

"If I am not clapped into a horrible German jail," she ventured encouragingly, "I may remember your kind invitation, and come here to look at the place."

"John Baptiste Quadro, a great architect from Italy, renovated the building in the second half of the sixteenth century, in the Renaissance style of course. The facade, the open arcades, and this beautiful ornamental section were the result of this architect's genius. In fact. . . ." The young man suddenly paused, his arm upraised, and looked at her, as if astonished to find himself talking. "But how inconsiderate of me, Madame. You are feeling the cold, and here I am giving a lecture on architecture. I'd better run for clothes for you and a coach."

Helena looked down at her torn dress and laughed. "Very well."

He stood up and started to leave, but stopped and turned suddenly. There was that awkward boyishness about him again. "But you won't move from here, will you? I'll be back in fifteen minutes."

"Of course not. I'm in your hands now, aren't I?" she said. "Don't you see, if I walk around in these clothes, someone will take me and lock me up in a house for the insane. That would be worse than a German prison, I should think."

"So you will wait for my return?" he insisted.

"I will wait."

Young Tadeusz had a cousin, Count Bozenta Chlapowski, who had seen a picture of Helena Modrzejewska in the daily *Kurier Warszawski*. He had at once fallen in love, and from that time on had followed with almost childish eagerness every appearance of Helena on the stage. It had become a sort of hobby. He was quite a wealthy man, and his aristocratic line went back several hundred years. Nevertheless he was regarded as dangerous by many of his own class. The Germans had reason to think so too. He had spent the previous year in a German prison for secret political activities. While in prison, this "pale Count Bozenta," as he was called by his friends and fellow prisoners, read all the plays he could lay his hands on in the prison library, in German, Polish, and French.

Count Bozenta was only too happy to hear from his cousin that Helena needed rescuing from a most precarious situation in the City Hall. He took her to the home of his family, patriots like himself. The eighty-year-old Dezydery Chlapowski was former aide-de-camp to Napoleon and a general of the Polish Army during the uprising of 1831.

The riot outside the theatre resulted in the loss of six Poles, shot down by German bullets. The whole town was in a state of dangerous tension, and armed police prowled about the streets in a fury. Old Dezydery Chlapowski visited the right quarters,

and greased the right palms at the City Hall. As a result the
Germans announced that they could prove no link between the
appearance of Helena in *Macbeth* with the regrettable demon-
strations of the people. Madame Modrzejewska, therefore, had
permission to leave the city.

After a few days' stay at the Chlapowski's, Helena set off
in the company of Count Bozenta. They passed through Czesto-
chowa. On the slopes of the Jasna Gora stood a monastery with
its miraculous picture of Saint Mary. Helena went in to pray.
From there they went through Cracow to the isolated, peaceful
Krynica, a resort which spread out at the foot of the Carpathian
Mountains, famous for its view, its healing springs, its wealthy
visitors, and beautiful women.

With the approach of the fall, Helena thought of visiting
Paris. As an excuse she spoke of her desire to increase her ward-
robe. Helena, who in her childhood had always loved to dress
up, now at twenty-six was not satisfied unless she was wearing
the very latest in Paris style. There was much talk on the subject in theatrical circles in Cracow, to Helena's pleasure, and
nothing could make her happier than to overhear some prominent ladies discussing in envious terms her success in leading the
fashion, or to hear one of them say, "I should like to have a
dress like Helena Modrzejewska wore on the street the other
day." Helena seemed to enjoy the whole business as a challenge.
As soon as someone else appeared in a gown similar to hers, she
would at once order a new creation from Vienna or Paris, so as
to remain in the lead.

Count Bozenta was amused. He had not left Helena's side
since the rescue from the Poznan City Hall. Now he eagerly
agreed to be her escort on this trip to Paris. He would be of
much use to her, she would see. And so he proved, by bringing
her immediately an invitation to appear at the Comédie Française, in a role in Racine's play *Iphigénie*.

The debut in Paris was an outstanding success. The critics,
with Paul de Saint-Victor at the head, had nothing but praise
for the Polish actress, and particularly remarked upon her
French diction which had no trace of a foreign accent. The
famous author George Sand showed her enthusiasm by going
back stage. Helena wrote back to her mother, "Pani Sand, smok-

ing her cigarettes continuously, had a very flattering chat with me. She praised my talent highly, and on leaving asked me if I would appear in her play *L'Autre*. The next day I was invited to her home for dinner."

After her performances, Count Bozenta would escort Helena to the restaurants of the Quartier Latin, where she would be pointed out by artistic circles as that beautiful Polish actress who had just taken Paris by storm. Then one evening, while at dinner, two gentlemen came up introducing themselves as Monsieur Duquesnel and Monsieur Chilly, directors of the Théâtre Odéon.

"It's incredible," wrote Helena to her mother, "how they implored me to appear in their play *La Loterie du Mariage* at the Odéon, offering me any salary I named. I don't know whether to refuse or accept."

Her young escort's prowess as a publicity agent was indeed phenomenal. Theatrical circles in Paris were quick to dub him a "Génie de la Réclame." The excited Helena knew full well that this last signal honor from one of the leading theatres in the capital was part of the work behind the scenes of Count Bozenta.

13.   THE LAST DATE

ONE AFTERNOON in early September of 1868, a young man sat sipping coffee at the Café Hawelko, his dark, intense features frowning over a pile of newspapers, Polish, French, and Viennese. This young man was known to most citizens of Cracow, and was looked upon with considerable respect as that young Jew whose skill with the brush had raised him to a most enviable position as painter of the aristocracy of Europe.

It was Igo Neufeld's custom to come to the Café Hawelko once every week or more to pore over the society columns in the more important newspapers, so that he could be well versed in the gossip among higher circles. These were the doings of potential clients, and Igo had long ago learned the necessity of winning clients rather than waiting for them to come to his studio.

On this day, he was eager to get back to work before the light faded, for he was in the middle of a landscape "for himself," besides having to prepare the background for a newly commissioned portrait. But his frown was more than usually marked. He was finding it hard to concentrate on what he was trying to read. His thoughts kept wandering to Helena. And he knew that it was jealousy once more that consumed him.

His burning love for the now famous actress had never dwindled, and for him it had seemed that the death of Gustav would clear the way for a lasting relationship between himself and Helena. They were both mature. They had both established themselves in their careers. His own earnings for his portraits were the talk of Cracow. Anyone could see that he lived comfortably, for besides his imposing studio on Grodzka Street, he kept the large suburban mansion on the wooded hilltop of Krzemionki, where he lived with his widowed mother. This house overlooked the whole of Cracow and the Vistula which seemed to hold the city in its everlasting embrace.

Igo was willing to make any compromises Helena wished if she would consent to live with him for the rest of his days as his wife. And yet he was making no headway. It was no secret in Cracow, and in other gossip-loving cities for that matter, that for the past three years, since the death of Helena Modrzejewska's husband, she had chosen the famous young artist as her escort whenever she stayed at Cracow. Because of the gossip their relationship had to be kept as secret as possible. Whenever Helena was in Cracow, Igo was forced to avoid his friends and acquaintances, pretend indifference, and even lie to their faces, in order to protect Helena from any unpleasantness.

Nevertheless, whenever Igo pressed the idea of marriage, Helena always managed to find a way out of saying yes. She would go off again on her trips to other theatrical centers, and leave him sunk in gloom and perplexity which he tried hard not to show to others. Then she would return, full of longing for him, and once again they would be supremely happy together. So the cycle would continue—their partings, their sorrow, her arrival and their reunion, and their goodbyes again—for three years, a torture for Igo. Sometimes it seemed to him that this situation would last forever, if only he could resign himself to accept such a relationship.

As he sat in the café, staring at newspapers with unreading eyes, he thought bitterly on these things. The relationship of lovers, no matter how sincere and how beautiful, was looked upon as a crime, for it had no sanction of a holy sacrament. But a marriage—ah, society looks upon a marriage, however soiled and unhealthy—no matter—still a marriage, a holy sacrament! Such was the wisdom of Cracow, and of course of the entire civilized world. Man likes to be legally cheated, and makes of it a sacred thing. It's what goes for morality, and who could oppose it in a lifetime. And what would be the use to try! That is the world—the world—the stupidity of the world! So it was— he, Igo, and his dear one must go on hiding from the gossips of the city, hiding their great love behind the walls of his studio or in his mother's house in Krzemionki.

But now there was something more to concern him. What was Helena doing while she was away from Cracow? There was that young Count, Charles Bozenta Chlapowski, who had made himself her manager. He was entirely too pushing. Why, that man was beginning to take credit for everything—every success of Helena's! And Helena was very close to him, it seemed . . . too close! He was handsome, that Count, and lean and refined. He looked like an English aristocrat, and owned enough wealth to compete with a Prussian baron.

Igo was so immersed in his thoughts that he was not aware of the approach of Jan Matejko, a young painter. Igo looked up with a start at the sound of the man's voice. He didn't want to speak to Matejko. He didn't want to speak to anyone. He was about to get up from the table, but he paused at the sound of Helena's name.

"You painted her portrait, didn't you?" Matejko was saying, his eyes prying into Igo's face. "I thought you might be interested. Here it is in the *Kurier Warszawski*. Evidently got it from the *London Telegraph*. Getting married, she is. And look who the lucky devil is, too." Matejko was thrusting the paper under Igo's chin. "Read for yourself."

Igo took the paper and read in silence. The young Count Bozenta Chlapowski, it was. He who had escorted Helena all over Europe in her tour of the great capitals, and acted with such extraordinary success as her theatrical manager, was now to be her manager for life. The story went on to say that rumors existed that they were already married.

Igo's face lost all color as he read. He handed the paper back to Matejko, muttered a hasty thank you, and stood up to go.

Matejko said quickly, "I heard a wonderful thing today. Something that Count Adam Potocki said—a former lover, you know." Matejko was almost whispering now. "Do you want to hear it?"

Igo paid the waiter for his coffee, and stepped away from the table. "No thanks. If Potocki loved her and got a refusal, it doesn't mean she was his mistress."

Matejko stared. Igo walked away. The man followed him, talking hurriedly. "But there's something in it, don't you think? After all she circulates only among the aristocrats. Listen to what Potocki said of her. . . ." Igo paused to open the door, and Matejko thought he had his attention. " 'A golden key fits every lock'—that's what he said. The lock, you see? Right, isn't it?" But Igo had a vacant look in his eyes and didn't seem to catch on to the most obvious wit. Matejko started to explain, "She's always running after an aristocratic golden key. You must agree there."

But Igo had already gone out. With each step he quickened his pace. He reached the end of Grodzka Street, ran into his studio, and threw himself face down on the couch. He lay there motionless for an hour, two hours, three, and the autumn evening approached. Clouds had gathered, and a dull drizzle came down on the crowds hurrying home. After a little while the streets became empty. A noisy wind from the foot of the Carpathians entered the city to shake the loose signs and rattle the loose windowpanes. Church bells sounded out the hour, mingled and clashed with the high notes of the Cracow trumpet. Together they contrived to shatter the monotony of the autumn rain that danced with the devilish mountain wind.

Inside the studio the darkness came, and the silence was broken only by the stirring of Igo on the couch. Slowly he got up and crossed to the window where the glass pane reflected his face, pale and gaunt. He stared at it absently, as if he expected some mercy to come out of the darkness beyond. A hope was brewing in his mind that Helena would come to him and offer some explanation.

In this frozen contemplation, he sat at the window for several hours more. From time to time his face was faintly lit by the yellow lamps of a passing carriage. It was Helena's way to knock at the window of his studio before coming to the door. He was used to the way she knocked. It was like the memory of a pleasant melody. But this evening, a disquieting and painful silence reigned.

The clock of the nearest church slowly struck eleven. Igo shook off his stupor and marched to the door. His thoughts were in a turmoil. He could not bring himself to believe that Helena had suddenly reversed her feelings about another marriage. For she had been with him here, in this studio, only eight days before, and she had made no mention of the Count. He had so despised himself for any recognized feeling of jealousy about

this Chlapowski fellow. How often he had argued with himself
—Chlapowski is useful to her; he has a good head for business
matters; she keeps him for that. And he? Why does he do it?
Well, the whimsical extravagance of a very rich man . . . how
else should he spend his money? It's natural—he gets excitement
out of it. And so on, until Igo had reassured himself by stubborn repetition. But now. . . . He must find out the truth!

He rushed out into the night, slamming the door behind him.
He was wearing no cloak or hat. He had forgotten about the
rain. It didn't matter. He rushed along the dark and empty
streets towards Szeroka Street. Madame Opid must know. Yes,
Helena's mother must know. The rain lashed his face. He could
feel the water in his shoes as he splashed through mud and
puddles. By the time he reached the Opids' house he was completely soaked. He knocked on the door for some time before
anyone answered. The lateness of the hour had not occurred to
him. After a while a light came on in the living room. Footsteps came to the door. It was Felix. He stood there in the hall,
holding up a lamp and peering at Igo in astonishment.

"Felix!" muttered Igo with a confused look on his face. As
he made no move, Felix pulled him into the hall. Igo stood there
stupidly, water streaming on to the floor, creating a widening
puddle.

Felix closed the door hastily. "Is something the matter, Igo?
You're soaking!"

"No, no!" said Igo quickly. "But you—what are you doing
here? Is it because. . . ."

"I've been ill," explained Felix gently, as he studied Igo's
face. "My heart, again, otherwise I should be at the theatre,
naturally." He made a gesture toward the living room. "But
won't you come in, Igo?"

Igo shook his head. His eyes were deep and staring. It was as
if his mind had become fixed, like a sleepwalker who has no
knowledge of where he is.

"Don't you want to come in, then?"

"No," said Igo. "No. Is Helena home?" His voice was
strangely flat. "I would like to congratulate her, for I hear she
is getting married."

"Oh!" Felix paused "Look, Igo, come in. Stay for a while and get dried out. I'll give you a drink."

"Is she in?" There was a dangerous brittleness to his voice.

"Why, no, she isn't. But. . . ."

"Is it true?"

"That she is getting married?"

Igo put out a hand and clutched Felix' arm. "Tell me the truth."

"Yes," said Felix softly. "The Count was here yesterday, and she confirmed the story."

Igo turned to the door, and before Felix could do anything to detain him, he was out of the house, rushing off into the dark rain.

Igo headed straight for Krzemionki, to his mother's home. He had the vague idea that Helena might be there. It was already two in the morning. Madame Neufeld was sleeping heavily after a hard day's work in the garden. The house was still, and only his former *niania,* the old maid Yaga, was up, on the chance that Igo might come in asking for something to eat or to drink.

Yaga greeted him anxiously, and had to tell him that Helena had not come to the house. Igo put his head down on Yaga's shoulder and wept sudden tears. She put her arms round him and rocked him a little, patting his soaked shoulder and stroking his wet hair. Igo should stay, should get out of his clothes and warm himself in front of the fire. She told him so; some sixth sense warning her that he was about to go out again as he was. When he started to pull away from her, she clutched at him wildly, and began to plead with him. But he rushed for the door, and dragged it open. She ran after him, trying to hold him. His arm made a wild sweep, catching her off balance so that she fell against a chair, and he was gone.

Treading stolidly along the muddy path, his breath coming in short gasps, like sobs, he crossed the meadow to the bank of the Vistula. His mind was in a frenzy, filled with the one desire to reach the treacherous waters and to plunge in . . . into these waters that some years back, on St. John's night, had cast such a terrible spell on him.

On the steps leading up to the door of Igo's studio on Grodzka
Street, the autumn sun came up to open Helena's eyes, tired with
so much weeping, and a wild fear came like a light in them.

The golden autumn of Poland is the most luxurious season
of the entire year, and in every way takes on the voluptuous
quality of Titian's women.

14. TIME IN WARSAW

I T WAS hardly a week after the strange disappearance of Igo. To be exact it was the twelfth of September, 1868. All Cracow was stirred by the magnificent ceremony that took place at the Church of St. Ann. A member of the wealthy aristocracy, Count Charles Bozenta Chlapowski, was lucky enough to win the hand of the beautiful actress, the pride of the city, Helena Modrzejewska. It was a major event in ancient Cracow's history. The papers were full of it—in Warsaw, in Vienna, in Paris. It was the main topic in the salons of Europe.

On the day after the wedding, the newly married couple abruptly left Cracow. Helena was filled with a desperate determination to put this place of her childhood out of her mind. Where was Igo? She did not care . . . she would not let herself care! She would erase from her memory this chapter of her past.

It was to Count Bozenta she had turned. He loved her, didn't he? And it was he who had done so much for her career. Her interests were his. He had devoted himself—yes, dedicated himself—to her genius. The European press, quite suddenly, had ceased to speak of her promising attributes as a great artist. Now, they headlined their columns: "A Great Tragedienne." And she was only twenty-eight.

The Russian administration made no habit of favoring gifted Poles in any field of endeavor, unless they were first judged absolutely reliable. They preferred mediocrities, who could be trusted to follow with unquestioning loyalty the dictates, however petty, of the foreign rulers. Nevertheless, Helena was invited by the Imperial Theatre of Warsaw, the capital of Poland under the Czar.

Helena signed a contract. Her basic salary was fixed at five thousand roubles a year, plus extra for expenses including all her costumes. She was even granted further privileges: the right to choose her own repertoire, to turn down any suggestions made by others, and the right to a special cut on box-office receipts from her annual show, called "Benefice." In a word, she had become the prima donna of the Imperial Polish Theatre and the queen of Warsaw's high society.

Some power at work behind the scenes had forced the ruling authorities to take notice of a leading Polish actress. It was mainly the work of one of the directors of the Imperial Theatre, a former actor by the name of Checinski. A persistent rumor existed that the sleek and handsome Pan Checinski enjoyed a benumbing romantic influence over Madame Maria Calergi Muchanoff. This was not true, for his sole and real love was the Polish theatre, and his sole aim to raise it to the highest standard of art and to keep it from becoming absorbed by the Russian giant. It was true, however, that he could not have succeeded in getting a contract for Helena without Madame Muchanoff's help.

This Madame Muchanoff, a tall and striking woman with lovely fair hair, was known for her extramarital adventures, but there was no one who would question her dedication to things theatrical. She had done much to establish her position of eminence in the field. She wrote reviews for the French press, mastered the main European languages, made her own appearance on the stage, and played the piano with unusual artistry. Among her friends she counted Fryderyk Chopin, whom she rescued many times from his earthly troubles. She was a friend to Franz Liszt, Richard Wagner, the Polish poet Cyprian Norwid, and to hundreds of other artists.

Her husband, the Baron Sergei Muchanoff, was the supreme supervisor of the theatres in Warsaw and a close friend of the Russian Count Buturlin, who represented the Czar's strong arm in Poland and was the head of the Warsaw Police. Buturlin and Muchanoff—these two dominated the social and cultural life of Warsaw.

The atmosphere created was not idyllic. The creaking boots of the Czar's police were heard not only on the streets, but everywhere—in the halls of the schools, in the churches, in the lobbies of the theatres. It was a constant reminder to the Poles of the words of Czar Alexander the Second: "Give up your dreams of freedom. All revolts will be crushed by our army."

The outspoken Madame Muchanoff was supposed to have said, while a guest of Count Chlapowski, that "she would light-heartedly exchange the Baron Muchanoff for a simple Pan Checinski." On the throne of the Czars she would put Shakespeare. In this way, she said, political life would be perfect, the world would be one vast theatre, and the artists in it would be the rulers, "for it is only artists who can be trusted to rule honestly." It was statements such as these that won so many Poles to her side. On the other hand, there were more than a few Poles who looked upon her with suspicion. Among them was Count Chlapowski who suspected her of spying among the Poles for the Czar.

The cream of Warsaw society came to the house of the Chlapowskis, the aristocracy of Poland and Europe, the famous Count Adam Potocki, the offspring of the ducal family of Radziwill, and many others. Count Bozenta had a weakness for titles and coats of arms and, despite his suspicions, Madame Muchanoff had to be invited. He would introduce her as "baroness" to his guests, and she would display offense at having her title used.

As for Helena, she made a point of attracting all the artists to her salons, even scientists and journalists. Frequent visitors were Zygmunt Wroblewski and Karol Olszewski, who some time later became known as "the Siamese twins of Polish science." Among the artists were the influential Adam Chmielowski, Stanislaw Witkiewicz, and Jozef Chelmonski, who lectured at receptions about the art of painting. Later, Chelmonski was to abandon painting, give all his money away, and put on the frock of a monk of St. Francis of Assisi. As "Brother Albert" he was to spend his life helping the poor. He was to found a church in the Carpathian Mountains, where he would go for meditation, a place he called nearer to God.

One of the guests Helena secured was a fellow actress of great stature, Adelaide Ristori, who was touring the European capitals in Shakespeare's plays. The two actresses were delighted to find much in common, for they both rebelled against the posturing, artificial type of acting and strove for naturalness and sincerity. As a result they were much alike in their portrayal of Mary Stuart.

When Madame Ristori was in town, Helena was able to invite Anton Rubinstein to her house, where he played his compositions and those of Chopin. The twenty-year-old Jan Reszke, whom Helena had introduced to music circles in Vienna, came to the Chlapowskis' and sang excerpts from *La Traviata*. This was a few years before his triumphal tour in the role of Alfonso through Venice, Rome, Paris, and London, a tour that started him on a great career in the leading role in such famous operas as *Carmen, Aïda, Romeo et Juliette, Lohengrin,* and *Tristan und Isolde.*

Helena's old friend Maurice Neville appeared on the scene again. He was still playing Shakespeare in English to the Polish of the rest of the cast, for he explained his Polish was not nearly good enough for Shakespeare, and anyway the audiences were not at all put out by the experiment. After all, art is universal, isn't it? Helena was very intrigued by his interpretation of Hamlet, which he frankly admitted he acted in the style of Edwin Booth.

For his part, Neville never ceased urging Helena to come to his own country, and before all her guests he would praise the beauties of America, especially California. He would gladden the hearts of the Poles by his talk of the free life, where no one was hindered from doing as he wished, from building his life as he wished, from saying anything he felt like saying about all and everything. The people of America, he said, were young and eager for experience. They hungered for culture. They longed to appreciate the finer things of life now that they were prosperous. They were searching for the good ways of spending their money. Neville painted a picture of vast audiences stretching from the Atlantic to the Pacific, waiting to receive the great artists of Europe. He would name off the teeming cities of plenty—New York, Philadelphia, Boston, Chicago, San Francisco. His listeners would sit silent before him, picturing in their minds this land of plenty, this paradise, this place of beauty, freedom, and riches, where no crushing foreign domination could exist, where no tyranny could arise. Art would flourish in that land. It would soon become the cultural center of the world. There grew a longing for the sight of American

Helena Modjeska (*Museum of the City of New York*)

Modjeska as Mary Stuart

Modjeska as Adrienne Le-
couvreur (*Museum of the
City of New York*)

Modjeska as Ca-
mille, 1878 (*Mu-
seum of the City
of New York*)

Minnie Maddern Fiske (*Museum of the City of New York*)

A caricature depicting (*from left to right*) Paprocki, Modjeska, and Charles Bozenta Chłapowski arriving in the United States, 1876

Modjeska as Rosalind, 1883 (*Museum of the City of New York*)

Sarah Bernhardt, as a sculptress, with a self-portrait head
(*Museum of the City of New York*)

Eleanora Duse, 1886 (*Museum of the City of New York*)

Otis Skinner, 1886 (*Museum of the City of New York*)

Mrs. Otis Skinner (Maud Durbin) (*Museum of the City of New York*)

Ethel Barrymore as a
child (*Museum of the
City of New York*)

Fanny Daven-
port (*Museum
of the City of
New York*)

Modjeska with her brother, Felix Benda, in Warsaw

Modjeska as Ophelia, 1892 (*Museum of the City of New York*)

Modjeska as Viola, 1892 (*Museum of the City of New York*)

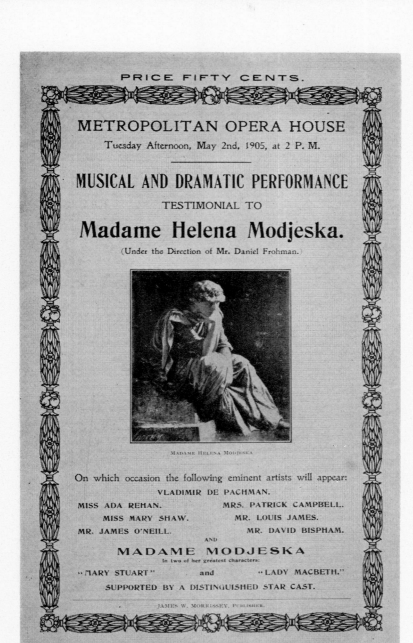

METROPOLITAN OPERA HOUSE

Tuesday Afternoon, May 2nd, 1905, at 2 P. M.

MUSICAL AND DRAMATIC PERFORMANCE

TESTIMONIAL TO

Madame Helena Modjeska.

(Under the Direction of Mr. Daniel Frohman.)

MADAME HELENA MODJESKA

On which occasion the following eminent artists will appear:

VLADIMIR DE PACHMAN.

MISS ADA REHAN.   MRS. PATRICK CAMPBELL.

MISS MARY SHAW.   MR. LOUIS JAMES.

MR. JAMES O'NEILL.   MR. DAVID BISPHAM.

AND

MADAME MODJESKA

In two of her greatest characters:

"MARY STUART"   and   "LADY MACBETH."

SUPPORTED BY A DISTINGUISHED STAR CAST.

JAMES W. MORRISSEY, PUBLISHER.

Program cover of the Testimonial to Modjeska at the Metropolitan
Opera House, 1905 (*Museum of the City of New York*)

Modjeska toward the end of her career

Modjeska in the garden of her California home

Funeral services for Modjeska, Cracow Cathedral, July 17, 1909 (*Culver Service*)

shores in the hearts of many of Helena's guests on these occasions, and, not the least, in Helena's.

She knew only too well from her own experience to what lengths the Russian censors would go to suppress the slightest manifestation of criticism or any hint of patriotism among the Poles, in literature or on the stage. She recalled how difficult it had been even for a person of such influence as Madame Muchanoff to persuade the authorities that it would be safe to allow a production of *Mazepa,* the drama of the great romantic poet Juliusz Slowacki.

Then, too, her husband was constantly under suspicion for his past underground activities, and because of a persistent rumor that he financially supported *Kraj,* a newspaper brought out in Austrian-occupied Cracow, critical of the Czarist regime in Russia and in Poland. Helena, too, was still in their bad books, because she toured endlessly throughout Poland, by sly means outwitting the local authorities in her work of educating the impressionable Polish audiences.

Madame Muchanoff fell ill. She had acted as a sort of protectress for Helena, her favorite actress. Now a subtle persecution started against Helena. She was constantly being blocked by annoyingly petty hindrances, and more and more rumors and suggestive gossip were being circulated about her in the Polish and Russian newspapers, stories about the love affairs of Helena. In one of the small theatres of Warsaw there was even a production of a farce attracting much attention. It was called *Nietoperze,* and purported to give excerpts of Helena's life. Interest in the mysterious disappearance of Igo Neufeld was far from dead. It was obviously being kept alive by deliberately circulated stories, the latest being that Count Bozenta and his wife, as well as Helena's mother, had plotted together the swift removal of an undesirable man.

The fact was the relationship between the famous couple was not without its storms. Helena, before her marriage, had told the Count the full story of her relationship with Igo, but it did not serve to soften his natural jealousy. Helena was used to receiving adulation from others. She began to feel hedged in by Bozenta's suspicions. There was the case, particularly trying, of the young writer Henryk Sienkiewicz. She admired his writing talent, and, as was her custom, she chose to help him in his career, to introduce him to influential people in the journalistic world. These attentions did not please her husband. He accused her outright of having a romantic interest in the young man. The storm raged. Helena left. She needed rest, and would go to the villa she owned at Zakopane in the Carpathians. The place had a glorious view of the great Giewont peak, and the sky seemed always a brilliant blue.

She was soothed by the grandeur of the mountains. She began to make of this villa her means of escaping the turmoil of Warsaw life—and of escaping the jealous scenes of her husband. But he would always come after her, somewhat repentant though unconvinced that his latest accusations had not been justified. And, at times, the ardent and imprudent young Henryk would appear on the mountain paths with the explanation that he was looking for material for a story.

During one of these trips to Zakopane, Helena fell sick with typhoid and was forced to spend several weeks in bed. Her half-brother, Felix Benda, came from Cracow, interrupting his performance in the Cracow Theatre, to be with Helena and care for her. He was shocked by Helena's words while she was in her fever, and on her recovery told her what she had said.

"You spoke of Igo all the time. You cried. You don't realize it, Helena, but you kept climbing out of bed, calling for him. Then you would scold him, and beg him not to pick flowers—flowers that were poisonous near the Vistula. Those words —*Igo—water—flowers*—you kept saying them over and over again. It was only by good fortune that your husband was not here at the time."

Helena was silent, lying exhausted in her bed, her eyes staring up at the pine boards of the ceiling. Felix knew that her love was for her eternal Igo. He had not questioned her decision to marry the Count, but he did not pretend to understand it.

As her silence continued, and he could see that she was lost in the past that she had tried so hard to escape, he tried to divert her mind to the present with news of her husband.

"You don't ask where Bozenta is, but he's been away for several days. I don't think he liked my coming here. Anyway, he went off muttering something about brothers, doctors, and servants being quite enough for you. But he had a reason for going. I've found out that young Henryk's in the mountains."

Felix waited for some sort of reaction from his sister, but as she gave him none, he went on. "That aristocratic husband of yours was out trailing Henryk. I learned that from a mountaineer friend of mine. He obviously wanted to find him in some ravine and beat him, or perhaps to push him off a cliff. Do you think I'm exaggerating? He followed him half way to Giewont . . . got tired then, and returned. Don't you think that's too much? That boy Henryk's in love with the history of the place and its literature—not with men's wives. Don't you think Bozenta's going too far?"

"An idiot!" Helena burst out, not lowering her eyes from the ceiling. Then, without turning her head, she reached out a hand for a leather-bound volume lying on her night table. It was Shakespeare. She opened the book and with her finger traced the lines, and Felix began to read:

> Trifles light as air
> Are to the jealous confirmation strong
> As proofs at Holy Writ.

This was the last meeting of Felix and Helena. He returned to the Cracow Theatre, and Helena to Warsaw. Their stage work kept them apart. They were both constantly engaged. And perhaps they had no need of words, for they understood each other over the distance; they felt each other's presence. Their natures were similar. They had the same heart, the same feelings.

A few more years and Felix Benda was dead of a heart attack in Cracow, after a performance. He had acted to the last moment of his life, and now left Helena to carry on alone. In that same year, 1875, Helena's greatest benefactress, Madame Muchanoff, passed from the earth. It seemed that fate had planned a hard struggle for Helena in a world peopled with those who could not understand her strange soul.

15. DESTINATION AMERICA

IT was not long before Helena's friends began to notice a change in her. Her customary vivacity was becoming clouded by fits of brooding silence. She began demanding more solitude. She would even lock herself up in her bedroom for long periods of time, refusing to eat. She slept very little. The healthy complexion that was so enchantingly youthful was fading. In fact, she had become the shadow of her original self. She made no effort to confide in anyone. Her one and only constant companion these days was her son Rudolph, now fourteen. She would take him with her on her occasional walks in the parks, or to the stores to buy him the books he wanted on painting or on dogs, for the moment his two pet subjects. Indeed, her devotion to her only child seemed almost an expression of fear, as if she were constantly reminding herself how swiftly his affections could turn elsewhere.

One evening in Warsaw in December, 1875, a group of Helena's dearest friends had succeeded in trapping her in her own house before dinner. Helena sat in the center of the living room. She sat back pale and tired in a comfortable armchair, while around her stood her friends leaning over her as they talked with great animation. Leon Kronenberg seemed to be the chief spokesman, but the others kept injecting words of encouragement, particularly young Henryk Sienkiewicz. The others were Sypniewski, Adam Chmielowski, and Lucjan Paprocki. Count Bozenta was in the dining room. With the help of Miss Albiett, who was giving Helena lessons in English, the Count was supervising preparations for dinner. His expression was one of complete boredom. He was too far away from the bedlam of sound in the living room to hear what was being said, despite the excitement of the voices. Finally there was quiet.

Helena looked up at her friends. Tears were in her eyes, and a faint smile played on her lips. Then she spoke in a subdued, almost humble voice. "I don't know that I could find the strength."

Young Henryk made a sweeping gesture with his whole arm. "Nonsense, your strength is the spirit in you. You will have America on their knees before you." Then he added in his characteristically boyish enthusiasm, "Why, I'm ready to go with you and carry you in my arms."

The others laughed. Even Helena joined them, and she replied archly, "I know you are ready, Henryk dear, but what would my husband have to say to that kind of transportation?"

"Well, we will ask him," cried Henryk, unabashed.

At that moment, Bozenta appeared at the door, and with a solemn expression, as though he were the butler in person, he announced, "Dinner is served. I say it myself because the butler has lost his voice."

The guests looked across at him, not knowing whether to laugh or be serious, but Kronenberg at once went up to him, took him by the arm, and led him to an adjoining room. "Eating *golabki* and *kielbasa* is not the only way to live," he was saying. Henryk couldn't resist following them, leaving the others to accompany Helena to the dining room.

"What is all this about, Leon?"

Henryk felt that Bozenta was in a dark temper, but Kronenberg waded right in.

"My dear friend, this is about that wife of yours. Surely you can see something is up. She's nervous, distraught. Why, she's never been so moody."

"Well?" The Count stood there with a frown on his handsome face. Henryk was suddenly aware of how gaunt he looked.

"All the stupid rumors of jealous people are troubling her," Kronenberg went on. "Her health is getting worse. Her nerves are strained to the limit. She is pale as death. Who knows what will become of her? Something must be done."

"You have a suggestion?"

The grandfather clock was ticking slowly in the hall. Kronenberg paused before an answer.

"Yes, my friend. A trip to America."

"What?" the Count almost yelled, stunned.

Henryk broke in quickly. "Next year there will be the Centennial Exposition at Philadelphia. That could be given out as the reason for her trip. Don't you think so?"

"Henryk," interposed Bozenta acidly, "won't you miss her?"

"I will miss you and Helena and her son," said Henryk blandly. "But her health is more important than anything else."

"A great sacrifice, Henryk," answered Bozenta.

"I adore her," said Henryk. "She is the goddess of the purest art, that is why. I wish she could live on forever."

Bozenta was silent, lost in thought. The others looked at each other, but both hesitated to add another word. Then the Count turned his eyes on Henryk, and spoke in a soft drawl. There was clearly an element of danger in it. "What if I agree? What if I do so with one proviso . . . that you, Henryk, go on ahead of us, and report back to us in writing, before we set sail?"

Kronenberg peered sharply at his host. Was it really necessary for Bozenta to set such obvious traps for Henryk? Did he think that the distance of five thousand miles would so easily solve the problem of Henryk's love for Helena? He looked at Henryk. The youth's eyes were shining with the excitement and the passion for life. There was no touch of discouragement in that face. And the words stumbled over themselves in their eagerness.

"Yes, yes, I'll go. I'll go for you. I'll make a place ready for you to stay in. You'll need a base . . . say in California, the place that American actor fellow is always talking about. It must be beautiful, beautiful enough even for Helena. And, you see, I'll gain something out of it, too. I'll get material together for a book about this fascinating country. See here, Bozenta, I will keep my word. I swear that on my soul, the soul of an artist. I'll expect the same from an aristocrat."

"So it is agreed?" put in Kronenberg quickly.

"Agreed," said the Count drily. The joke—if joke it was— about aristocrats did not suit his taste.

"Fine," confirmed Henryk, as he turned elated toward the door.

During dinner, Henryk caught the warning look of Kronenberg and kept silent. Finally Bozenta announced the news to his wife and to the rest of the company in a casual way, as though it had been his own idea.

Everyone reacted with vast approval, with the exception of Helena herself. Paprocki and Sypniewski even offered to go with them. Such positive enthusiasm, and the apparent willingness of her husband, gradually broke down Helena's resistance, so that by late evening she was agreeing to the idea, provided she could take Rudolph with her and provided her performances in America were not exclusively for the Polish population.

She was given no time to change her mind, for her friends went right to work arranging an American tour. True to his word Henryk left first, to prepare the way, and for the others passage was booked for July. Helena Modrzejewska, with her husband and son and friends, would sail from the German port of Bremen.

The guiding light in all these preparations had been the skillful and kind-hearted Leon Kronenberg, and in the *Kurier Warszawski,* June 20, 1876, appeared an article from the editors apparently inspired by him:

Is it really true that she leaves us tomorrow? But where is she going? It is said that she leaves for America. But is that really true? It is said that the reservations on the boat have already been made, that she will stay there six months—perhaps a year. And she is going to Philadelphia? No, no—to Chicago. Is that it? And there she will play before Americans? Good! But in what language? Polish or English? And how will our own stage do without her for so long a time? This great actress, this true genius of the stage!

These were the questions people were asking themselves and one another yesterday evening. Come what may, the fact is that Madame Modrzejewska played last night in the Letni Theatre for the last time before her departure for a vacation which begins today. For this performance, she chose two scenes from Shakespeare: the balcony scene from *Romeo and Juliet* and Ophelia's mad scene from *Hamlet.* Besides these, she did the last act from *Adrienne Lecouvreur,* together with the whole of *Sluby Panienskie* of Aleksander Fredro. It is probably unnecessary to re-echo the praises repeatedly showered on this great actress for her unique interpretations. We wish only to remark that her last performance, providing in one evening so many distinct sensations, so many soaring concepts, will long remain in the memory of those fortunate ones, who after a victorious battle to the box office, succeeded in getting tickets. They were privileged to admire a whole series of roles so diverse and yet so expertly accomplished, that any theatre would find it hard to undertake, except perhaps one or two of the most distinguished European stages having the best actresses in the world to work with.

The enthusiasm of the audience reached the greatest heights. Bursts of applause greeted the actress at the finish of every scene, and there seemed to be no end to the curtain-calls she received. This ovation closed on a note of hope that she would return to us soon, and that she would shine on our stage for a long time to come. We do not doubt that this will come true, and we pin our hopes on the future.

After the performance, the audience *en masse* formed a double row stretching from the stage doors of the theatre, through the length of the park to the main gate, waiting for sight of the actress. On her appearance she was greeted with a new round of applause and shouts of "Come back to us soon, for there's no one to take your place." And indeed it is true, there is no one to be found who can take the place of one we have come to regard as the main pillar of both tragedy and comedy. The lover of plays will be lonely without this actress, who during her stay in Warsaw brought to our stage the masterpieces of the greatest writers of the world, adding to their value the power of her own genius.

Moved to tears by this marvelous display of appreciation and sympathy, Madame Modrzejewska gave her promise to return. . . . But when?

16. THE PAST FOLLOWS

THEY PUT up at the Hotel Cordelia in Bremen—
Helena, her husband and son, and their friends,
Paprocki and the Sypniewski family. It was on the eve of their
sailing. A letter had come to Helena from Henryk Sienkiewicz.
He was in San Francisco. His letter was a song of joy of the
marvels of the Golden West. Henryk had a happy way with
words, whether on his tongue or through his pen. He could
always stir Helena to excitement by his own vast enthusiasms.
And now she found herself filled with a strange longing to get
away from Warsaw, Vienna, Paris, the whole complex scene of
Europe, with its throttling traditions, its aristocracies and ap-
palling poverty, and to buy a farm in California, settle down
on the land and cultivate oranges and grapes and vegetables, to
mix with the simple people of the earth, and to enjoy the bright,
invigorating warmth of the sun by the sea.

Would she give up her acting career? What had it brought
her but the admiration of masses of people she did not know
and could not know? What of her own life and feelings? How
had she lived? Had she lived at all since the disappearance of
Igo?

She was oppressed by her thoughts as she walked the lobby
of the Hotel Cordelia. She had not noticed a precise, quiet-
spoken, elderly man, who had come up beside her. His voice
seemed so close to her ear that it startled her. She turned to
him, hesitating, as he bowed to her slightly with a face that
was totally expressionless.

"Madame Modrzejewska," he was saying to her in a somewhat harsh French, "I am Gustav's brother, Heinrich Sinnemayer."

Helena stared, unable to speak. It was like the sudden reappearance of the past. She began to picture Gustav in this man.
There was something softer in the man's face, and there was a
sorrowful look in the eyes, that made him almost appealing.

137

Gustav was younger, he cared less. He had never suffered like that.

"You must forgive me, please, for the manner of approaching you," the man continued, obviously put out by her silence. "I was not near Cracow when my younger brother died. Since then I have heard so many stories on the cause of his death, most of them unpleasant, and most of them conflicting, that I am left without anything I can or want to believe."

Helena found her voice at last. "Well, what is it I can do?"

"Madame, from what I have heard about you and from what I now see, I can only reject most of these ugly rumors that seek to defame your character. And yet your former husband was my brother, and I long to hear the story from your own lips, for you alone, I feel, can give me the truth about Gustav, and set my mind at rest again."

How strange, thought Helena, that this man should come just now and want to stir up all the past, when she was on the verge of fleeing from it in a desperate search for something new, something she could find faith and pleasure in. "I don't know how honest I am," she began. "So many things change about us, and change us. But I will tell you what I know. Come over by the window. No one will disturb us there."

The old man followed Helena, and sat stiffly in an armchair opposite her as she told her story. The back of the armchair was very high. It made him seem small and wizened. He kept his grave eyes on her, his face expressionless, until she began to forget his presence, and seemed to be reliving her experience in her thoughts.

"Gustav died—I don't know how. For I was not with him then. I can only swear before heaven that I was not in any way responsible for his end. You must understand he had a great many enemies. If he didn't die from natural causes, then. . . . It is so possible. I didn't realize until very late. . . . I was such a child! So young! He knew me as a child. He taught me everything during those years of my growing, and he taught me to accept my future marriage to him as my inescapable destiny. I was made to think that my life wouldn't open up to the beauty and the joy of new things in a new world, that my talent would be buried and wasted, without his aid. I was young and religious and susceptible. And he was so much older and apparently so much wiser than myself. And he was so very kind to my mother. He won her completely over to his side, so that his wishes became hers. Poor Mother! And together they dictated the pattern of my thoughts.

"I was in love with a boy who wanted to marry me, but Gustav was deeply jealous of Igo and resorted to all kinds of subterfuge to turn me against the boy. I say I was young and innocent and I was ambitious. I had no defense against the cleverness of Gustav. Bit by bit he poisoned my soul, to gain possession of me. Am I exaggerating? All the natural instincts of girlhood were taken from me. To take their place I was given a way of life that has made me false. After years of rather hell than marriage—when Gustav was already gone, and I had the chance to marry Igo—I found—oh, it is so hard to believe!—that all my values were false. I was incapable of making the decision that could have brought me a truthful happiness. . . .

"Gustav did this. He distorted things. He kept the truth from me. I didn't know about his business affairs, the chaotic, unfeeling way he worked for his own advantage. Outsiders would come to me and inform me of his underhanded deals and his exploitation of others . . . everything for himself. Even me—he didn't work for me, but only to keep me. It seems that God must have punished him. . . . How he died, I don't know. But it was the way he lived—in secrecy. My conscience is clear as far as he is concerned. He cannot touch me any more. He distorted my life. . . . May God forgive him. . . . But I lost forever my true love. I didn't have the strength—was that it?— how poisoned! . . . to return to Igo. . . ."

She stopped. Her voice seemed to fade away, as if in a dream. Had she forgotten the old man before her? He got up and kissed Helena's hand. She saw in his eyes an expression of terrible sadness, but the face maintained its masklike quality, and he said no word. He quietly left the room.

It took thirteen days to cross the Atlantic. The ocean to Helena was something new and fascinating. While the others in her party were sunning themselves on the deck, she would hang for hours over the side of the boat watching the waves.

The higher the waves, the better she liked it, or rather the more drawn to them she became. What was a human life here? She felt the whole ship shudder at the smack of the ocean's great hand. She stared down into the dark sea, and felt her own problems sinking, drawn into the depths and out of her, leaving her in a strange state of free elation, a clear-headed madness. Whenever nostalgia seized her, made her thoughts turn back to the old and familiar, she would hasten down to the ship's chapel and pray before the image of Christ. But it was the rage of the sea that could best wash her free again. It was a monster that held her enchanted. It terrified her, but held her spellbound. She was reminded of the dragon of the castle of Wawel. She would never forget the ocean. She would have to live near it.

Helena's first response to New York was that it appeared like "a monstrous and untidy bazaar." But on the second day she had already changed her mind. She had begun to look around. The city was unique, she thought. Germans, Italians, Scandinavians, Irishmen, Poles—all living side by side, accepting their freedom and equality without question. That she adored. Yes, this was a real city.

The arrival of so prominent an actress from the other side had not been overlooked by Henry Abbey, one of the most astute producers in America. The Chlapowskis barely had time to get themselves settled at a hotel on Fifth Avenue before the affable and disarming Mr. Abbey presented himself at their door. He glowed all over with pleasure, for he found Madame Modrzejewska in excellent spirits. She liked New York? Ah, but there are other cities as fair as New York. Madame must see the mall. And, of course, the American people must see her. They are all waiting to see her. She will receive the greatest ovation in history.

Helena smiled, and shook her head. How beautiful she is, thought Mr. Abbey. But is she really modest, or just acting the part for my benefit? But anyway—charming, all charmingly done. But to business. . . .

"You think I am saying that to please you, Madame. But I do not exaggerate in the least. I am a man of business. And as a man of business, I come to you now. Please understand that the offer I shall make to you is only a business offer. I am but using the knowledge I have of the American people, and I expect to make money on it, naturally. A contract speaks facts, not flattery."

Helena put up a graceful hand. There was a look of surprise on her face, and she spoke in French, "Let us not talk of business contracts, Mr. Abbey. I am here to enjoy myself. That is all."

Henry Abbey stared. He sat up straight in his chair. He had had experiences often enough with shrewd artists, who would pretend disinterest in an offer to get a better one. But this Helena Modrzejewska—she should change that name somehow; no one will be able to pronounce it—she was already protesting before she had even heard what his offer was.

"But, Madame," he began again, "leave it to me and I will organize the whole thing. You may play your great roles, your Shakespearean roles. I will name you some of the towns you will play in, the biggest cities throughout the nation—New York, Philadelphia, Baltimore, Chicago, Boston, Springfield, St. Louis, New Orleans, Memphis, Cleveland, Pittsburgh, and even across the border into Canada."

She was smiling at him, with her beautiful eyes. She seemed about to stop him again. He hurried on. He always liked to get to the point fast. But this time he was beginning to feel rushed. If only he could tell whether or not she was playing with him.

"I offer you five hundred dollars a night. And further, if the total proceeds on a night exceed four thousand, that excess, Madame, will be divided between us. There will be no expenses for you. Traveling, hotels—I will take care of all that. There. I make this offer to you because I wish to have the rare honor of presenting you to the American public. Only in this way will my name go down in history."

He spread out his arms, just a touch of the histrionic, then learned back in his chair as if he had spent himself. Only his eyes showed his watch for the effect on her.

There was a look of astonishment on her face now. She seemed to hesitate.

"Yes?" he said encouragingly, gently.

She leaned a little toward him. "Dear Mr. Abbey," and her

French was of the caressing kind. Henry Abbey stirred deliciously. "I am really touched by this proposal. You are most kind to me. But, you see, there are two reasons why it must be no. First, I don't speak English well as yet. And second, I don't have the strength to act any more—not for some time. I am tired. In fact, I am going to California, Mr. Abbey, to settle there on a farm. I am going to live quietly and take a long rest."

Mr. Abbey's eyebrows shot up. "Amazing!" Was it possible that an actress of such fame could do such a thing? Faced with such an offer! Throw away thousands of dollars just to retire! So young and so beautiful! And on a farm, of all places! No! It was unbelievable! More—it was unreasonable! "So, maybe you will agree to appear in *Adrienne Lecouvreur.* We have all heard of your success in that role created by Scribe and Legouve. You yourself have made it famous. So play that only, and we shall see what will happen later."

"Mr. Abbey, I would not play before the American public except in English, and my English is extremely limited. I assure you, Mr. Abbey, that the present time, in my present state of mind, I do not intend at all to appear on the stage."

This couldn't be anything but sincerity, he decided at last. At least for this morning. He sighed helplessly. He must have come on the wrong morning.

She laughed a little. She was laughing at his perplexity. "Perhaps," she said, "I will change my mind some time later, but not now."

That was the clue he wanted, he decided, and promptly reappeared the next day. It was quite early in the morning. Helena came into the room, escorted by her husband. Abbey avoided mention of contracts. He had his campaign all worked out.

"Before you start out on your trip to far off California with its changeable climate, now sunny, now rainy"—a slight accent on the last word—"I would be most happy to show you around the East, while you are in New York."

The actress turned her eyes on him and laughed, good-naturedly but as if she could see clear through him.

"What a splendid idea!" enthused the Count, helping to close the trap. It happened that he was a fervent hunter and an expert on firearms. He wished to be taken to see the Colt factories.

"Fine," said Abbey quickly, "we'll start tomorrow for Hartford in Connecticut. That's where the factories are. I invite you as my guests. I'll be here tomorrow with the coach and horses at eight."

Bozenta Chlapowski was loud in his gratitude. Abbey turned to Helena.

"Won't you stay for breakfast?" she said. "I'll prepare a Polish meal for you if you will stay."

Abbey was delighted. He felt he was making headway. The two men chatted while Helena was occupied in the kitchen. Most of the talk was on Abbey's side, for he wished to sound Chlapowski out. Did he agree with his wife's ambition to live on a farm? It quickly appeared that the idea of farming was not the Count's, although he was far from opposing it. He agreed, nevertheless, to try a little persuasion on his wife, to induce her to reconsider the American stage proposal. Further, Abbey suggested that Helena's stage name should be abridged to Modjeska. The Count agreed that Modrzejewska was too difficult for the English-speaking tongue, but he did not know how Helena would feel about it. He would try to sound her out.

The door opened, and Helena made her entrance in a new blue gown. Her copper-colored hair, combed in locks at the front and fastened delicately upward in the back, created in Abbey's mind the illusion of a pretty doll with large, round, black eyes.

Behind her was the maid, Hanusia, pushing a wagon laden with dishes. Abbey marveled at the display. There were Polish sausages, ham and eggs, baked potatoes, great chunks of cheese, radishes and *nalesniki* pancakes with preserves prepared *à la Polonaise*. In the center stood prominently a bottle of French wine, surrounded by layers of sliced pumpernickel bread and pastries from an old Polish bakery on St. Mark's Place.

Was this a Polish breakfast? Helena smiled at the expression on Abbey's face. "Oh, you mustn't think that all Poles eat so large a breakfast. It's just that we've got in the habit of eating our largest meal in the morning." Then she added with a laugh, "You may eat it without hesitation, dear Mr. Abbey, for the food is all American. The only thing I brought from Warsaw are the silver table cover and . . . Hanusia."

Abbey exploded with laughter. Yes, he would eat, and eat well. Helena took his praises with the pleasure of a child. Her passion for cooking had taken hold of her in the past year or so. She regarded it as an art. Abbey was intrigued but mystified. Could it really be that she intended to sacrifice her stage career for this!

The next day, Rudolph was left to the care of the Sypniewski family. They were all going on a sight-seeing tour of New York, including rowing and fishing on the Hudson River. As for Helena and her husband, their visit to the Colt factories was a real success. Abbey had already passed the word along, and as a result Helena found herself greeted by a throng of factory workers, who had immigrated from Poland. In her honor they sang Polish songs. Helena was moved to tears, as she turned to Abbey.

"How strange life is," she said. "Here in America a foreigner can sing in his own language, and is even encouraged to do so by the factory manager. But in Poland, no! It is absolutely unthinkable that any worker in a Polish city, in Lodz, Poznan, or Warsaw, could sing in his own tongue, even after work. Think of it . . . a man forbidden to sing in his own language on his own soil, and here. . . ."

The climax of her tour of the Colt factories was the honor of firing the first shot from a newly constructed cannon.

From Hartford, Abbey took the Chlapowskis to Boston where he had arranged a reception for Helena from the small Polish colony. His idea was to make her feel as much at home as possible. Then, since she had spoken of farming, there must be a strong love for the rural aspects. Later they visited Thomas Edison in Menlo Park. Abbey took her to Niagara Falls, and watched her stand lost in wonder, gazing down on the great sweep of water, her blowing hair like flames against the vast blue of the sky, and he felt satisfied that he was achieving his aim, that of holding her in the East. True, she had said nothing about changing her mind, but a well-to-do Polish family had invited the Chlapowskis to stay a few weeks at their home in Gardner, Massachusetts, and when the Count had urged it Helena had agreed. So there would be a few more weeks' grace.

For his part, the Count Bozenta was far from optimistic. He had more experience with Helena's determination when she had made up her mind to anything. He had already tried to convince her of the need to find some source of income in America. Both he and his wife were accustomed to a high standard of living, which in the United States was ten times more costly than in Poland. In his own country, Bozenta was considered a wealthy man, but then most of his wealth was tied up in estates. Was he to start selling land now? To whom? He could always sell to the German and Russian land-grabbers, but that he would never do, and there were no Poles who could afford to buy more land. From his wife's savings and by selling some of their family jewelry they managed to amass around twenty-three thousand dollars. Helena was delighted. For her, that was enough. Enough to buy a farm in California, yes. But Bozenta was able to see that it would leave them little beyond. And what would they live on?

On the farm, was Helena's glib reply. But what did she know about running a farm? She would be far wiser to take his advice and accept Henry Abbey's offer first. Five hundred a night! Why, at that rate, in the matter of two months they could make up far more than twenty-three thousand. This way they could at least live in comfort, without anxiety, while they were getting the farm in working condition. But these calculations made no impression on Helena. The one enthusiasm for the moment was the prospect of life on a farm. All other considerations were petty and beneath her.

Bozenta was sunk in despondency. He had lost all influence over his wife. She had changed, he felt. Her whole attitude toward life had changed. Where was that old flaming ambition? Her worship of her art? Where was her affection toward him? He thought of the word *affection*—for now it seemed to him that Helena had never truly felt love for him. Only for that Igo Neufeld who was supposed to have drowned himself for love of her. This Igo must have lacked courage and stamina. An unworthy fellow! What could Helena have seen in him? But he, Bozenta, could not answer that. What did Helena see in this

Henryk Sienkiewicz? Now sitting in California, waiting for
her! Writing eager letters to her! Did she want to go West
and live on a farm for that? For Henryk?

And Bozenta found himself tortured with jealousy again,
and in this wretched state of mind, he was unable to think out a
solution to his problems.

Abbey's final enticement came in the shape of the free use of
his home in Connecticut for a whole year. But it failed. Helena
would not change her mind. The one and only concession she
made to the wishes of the charming Mr. Abbey was the agreement to change her name to Modjeska, to make it easy for the
English-speaking tongue. Mr. Abbey could only shake his head,
baffled. Of what use was it if she was forsaking the theatre for
a farm?

17. PRELUDE IN SAN FRANCISCO

A LL ARRANGEMENTS were made. Helena and her party would sail from New York by steamer, cross the Isthmus and follow the coast to San Francisco. Bozenta had made several attempts to oppose the trip, but only succeeded in making their relationship still more strained. Helena was not listening to her husband. She was reading the letters from Henryk. Henryk had even organized a joint letter with several Polish residents begging her to come to them. A Polish colony was flourishing on the West Coast, made up of those families who had escaped their country after the insurrections of 1831 and 1863 and had found haven in California. It was their hope, the joint letter explained, to establish a center of Polish culture there. The name of Helena Modrzejewska, now Modjeska, would be a rallying point for this undertaking. Let her but present a few plays and the attention of the world would be turned upon their efforts.

Bozenta wondered. Does she intend to play in California? Then why not New York? Why not with Abbey and his five hundreds? The quarrels between them grew. Helena was already upset by the sudden illness of Rudolph. She worried until she fell ill herself, and the doctors spoke of neurasthenia and kidney troubles. It postponed their sailing for several weeks.

At last they set off, on board the S.S. *Crescent City* bound for the Isthmus. Helena was taciturn, accessible to no one except her son. At the Isthmus, the passengers changed to another ship, the S.S. *Constitution,* long past its prime and more ready to be turned into scrap than to be carrying important passengers. The Pacific sailing became, in the sticky heat, a painful ordeal. The food was appallingly bad, while the sanitation facilities made Helena nauseous.

On arrival they found San Francisco, with its flourishing Polish colony, a place of great charm. Henryk Sienkiewicz, staying with a Polish friend, Julian Horsin, showed Helena around, with streams of enthusiasm for everything. He introduced her to all the prominent figures in the colony, some Polish immigrants, other people of Polish extraction. Among the latter were Zbigniew Brodowski, former American Consul to Germany; General Krzyzanowski, who had distinguished himself in the American Civil War by a magnificent cavalry charge at Chattanooga; and Captain Coon, former Confederate officer, friend, and adviser to the General. Then there was Edward S. Solomon, former governor of Washington Territory, who conversed in a broken Polish coupled with an energetic sign language of his own making.

Helena busied herself during the next few months with the purchase of an orange plantation and with her English lessons, under the tutelage of an enthusiastic admirer, Jo Tucholska, who despite her pride in her Polish ancestry spoke no Polish. She did so well with Helena that the actress was soon speaking of trying out her English on the stage. Henryk passed the word along. General Krzyzanowski and Governor Solomon rushed to the manager of the most outstanding theatre in the city—the Grand Opera House. The manager, Barton Hill, confessed he was interested, but first he would have to listen to her himself. After all, her reputation had not been established on American boards. She must come to the theatre and act something for him.

This was quickly agreed to, and on the day of the "tryout" the first few rows of the theatre were occupied by Helena's closest friends, triumphant and elated over the prospect of hearing their divine artist again. In their midst sat the manager with his henchmen, assuming a note of appropriate objectivity. Helena made her entrance and started to speak. The manager stirred in his seat. After a few minutes he was heard to say somewhat loudly, "But she's no good!"

Helena's friends gasped in horror. Helena stopped. She had heard him. She let out a sigh, and choked it off. Tears were in her eyes as she cried out, "Gentlemen, gentlemen, what have you exposed me to?" With that she ran behind the scenes.

Brodowski, who was to give his own description of this fiasco, speaks of Helena's friends in the audience as sitting quite stunned by what had happened, as if some sentence of

death had been passed. The first to recover from the shock was
the General who sprang to his feet bellowing that the manager
was a blockhead and an idiot, and should be the last one to pass
judgment on so elevated an artist.

There was a general rush backstage to reassure the distraught Helena, but she insisted that it was a "humiliation,"
that she would hear no more of the whole business, and would
go back to her farm. Her friends clustered around her, protesting. Besides, they wanted to tell her that Governor Solomon
had a new plan already worked out for a new rehearsal. This
experience would not happen again. They would see to that.
Henryk Sienkiewicz became his explosive best with his passionate entreaties. But Helena would have none of them. She
had made up her mind. Bozenta shrugged his shoulders in despair. What a farce! To throw away a great career and thousands and thousands of dollars—all for one asinine critic! And
the whole campaign to center the attention of the world on Poland's plight was falling to pieces!

At this point in the general anguish, it was old Captain Pio-
trowski who came to the rescue. He drew himself up in front of
Helena, and with a challenge gleaming in his eyes, he snapped,
"Well, Madame, if such a scoundrel is able to put you to rout,
I say then you are no woman of Poland."

Helena blanched and dropped her hands from her face. The
old soldier had touched her pride. In the moment's silence that
followed, she put out her hand to him, and turned to the others
with great solemnity. "As you say then," she said. "My friends,
do what you want with me."

John McCullough, at this time, was past seventy. He had
had a long and vivid stage career, and was now the manager
of one of the theatres in San Francisco, the Baldwin Theatre.
McCullough was intrigued at the chance of hearing the much-
discussed actress from Europe. He was prepared to be skeptical.
He had heard of the Grand Opera House incident, and would
see for himself. But he wanted her at her best, not laboring
under handicaps. He would hear her in her own language. He
would like to hear her in one of her Shakespearean roles. Let
her be thoroughly at home. This way he could make a true judgment of her talents.

Again Helena's entourage of Polish friends accompanied her to the theatre. But this time they went with none of their former boastfulness. They had no doubts about the genius of Helena, but in their hearts they feared they might have misjudged America and its capacity for artistic appreciation. Perhaps this McCullough, even though himself an actor of some prominence, might be but another Barton Hill.

Helena had chosen the balcony scene from *Romeo and Juliet*. She walked on the stage. Her voice was sweet, delicate, and touching. Her friends listened to the sound of their language on the stage pouring out in such expressive loveliness, and they were transported with joy. The old Captain began to stir uncomfortably beside Henryk, clearing his throat most oddly. Henryk hissed in his ear, *"Sza. Cicho.* Be quiet!" Then the General began to fidget, pretending something had got in his eye. They were all so deeply moved that they had forgotten the manager completely. McCullough was not to be seen. He was standing in the wings. Suddenly the old man, his white hair streaming, rushed out on the stage, clasped Helena's hand, and fell on his knees. "You are the greatest artist I have ever seen. America will worship you."

McCullough would not let her leave his theatre. First she had to sign a contract for a series of twelve performance at the Baldwin.

It was on the 13th of August, 1877, that Helena Modjeska made her first public appearance on an American stage, playing the leading role in *Adrienne Lecouvreur* in English. The theatre was filled to capacity with an eager audience. In the middle of the play, the actress narrowly missed permanent injury when the veil she was wearing caught fire. But order was restored and the play went on. It was a complete triumph. The applause was deafening, and the next day the press sealed her "victory."

It was not long before Helena was beseiged with offers. The young actor Edward Ward, who wished to take his Company on a tour through the Western states, offered to put her at the head of the troupe and finance the whole undertaking. They would do such plays as *Adrienne Lecouvreur, La Dame aux Camélias,* and *Frou-Frou* by Victorien Sardou. Then the out-

standing theatrical agent, Henry Sargent, offered her a contract
for two years to appear in theatres across the entire country
and in Canada. But Helena refused all these offers. She went to
old John McCullough, who had come to look upon her as
though she were his own daughter, and kissed him goodbye.
She was going back to her farm in Anaheim in Southern California. But first she had to tell him that it was he who had restored her faith in humankind.

18. ANAHEIM UTOPIA

BOZENTA COULD hardly take offense at Henryk being there. So thought Helena, as she caught sight of the young writer striding out to the orchard. There was always need of added hands on the farm, with its vast acres of orange trees, its grape vines, and vegetable fields, and Henryk worked willingly, if erratically, and was content enough to sleep in the shed where Paprocki was, for want of space in the five-room ranch house. Far off she could see the other men in the fields, her husband, Sypniewski, Paprocki, and her son, Rudolph, who at sixteen was nearly a man. They had been out there working since five-thirty, and soon would be coming back looking for breakfast.

Henryk was late that morning, but then he had probably been finishing a new story. His walk was brisk, with that air he assumed when he had just completed some writing project to his liking. And look how he was laughing at the two Sypniewski children running on either side of him. Yes, she was getting to know his every mood.

Feeling a peculiar elation that she attributed to the early morning air, Helena finished her dressing and hurried downstairs to where her maid Hanusia was waiting. Each morning at six they would drive the cows to the barn and milk them. The two women would then rush back to the kitchen to prepare breakfast for ten people. It was not a simple task. For in this ideal commune, as she thought of it, everyone wanted something different for breakfast; one scrambled eggs and *kielbasa,* another ham with fried potatoes and mushrooms, another wine soup, *kluski* with salt pork, and so on. And always there must be black bread, sour milk, tea, coffee, and various fruits.

"Oh well," laughed Helena to herself as she worked at the stove, in her best flowered Polish apron, "in one's own cottage even smoke is pleasant."

There were hammocks strung outside the house among the

shade trees, and it had become the custom for the amateur farmers to lie in them for half an hour or so after breakfast, smoking, talking a mile-a-minute, boasting of their achievements out in the fields, and arguing over plans for the future harvest. But the women went on working, tending to the pigs and chickens, and doing other chores around the house. From this they were compelled to go straight into the preparation for lunch. Sypniewski's wife was unable to help as she had been ailing for some time and was indeed too much of an invalid to tend to her own children.

For Helena there was always some time to herself between lunch and supper when she would work on her pastoral poems in praise of the glorious West. She felt that all she needed was sincere determination and hard work.

Supper was at sundown, prepared in the Polish manner, beginning with *barszcz* as a soup, *pierogi* with cheese, roast chicken with vegetables, fruit compotes, honey, and wine. Then all would gather in the living room, the largest room in the house. With its oil paintings and large family photographs brought from Europe, it had an air of old-world dignity about it. Rudolph would sit at the piano and play Chopin and Moniuszko surprisingly well, and they would all think of the old country, the waving fields of rye perhaps, on the Mazowsze plains, the ancient province of Poland.

Often Helena would recite a part of Adam Mickiewicz' long poem *Pan Tadeusz,* or possibly something from that other great national poet Juliusz Slowacki. She liked to turn to Henryk then and get him to read his latest story or some sketch concerning the United States, that was ready to be sent on the next day to the Warsaw newspaper.

At times Helena would sing songs in French, German, and Polish, her clear voice soaring out through the open windows and over the fields, like the chiming of bells. The little town of Anaheim, besides its Spanish families, had a large number of German immigrants who worked on the neighboring farms, and often these humble German people would gather on the roads to hear the songs of their homeland sung at the house of the Poles.

And always at her feet sat Henryk, so deeply moved he could

not speak, only nodding his head when the others asked for more. At times Helena felt herself drawn to him, this gifted youth—already thirty, but still giving out the sense of youthfulness—whose soul was in his eyes. Almost without knowing it, she would sing her songs to him, as if the others were not present. Only when she had finished and received the applause of her friends did she suddenly observe the terrible coldness of her husband. Yet what could she do? Henryk adored her, was prepared to do anything for her. All the coldness of her husband would not shake him off. And everyone else had become used to Henryk's passionate presence, ceasing to find anything extraordinary in his exaggerated romanticism. Nevertheless, Helena was becoming aware of a growing boldness in Henryk's behavior. It was almost as if he were acting from sheer bravado, daring the Count to take offense.

Helena admitted to herself that she did nothing to discourage such a development. In a way she too was defying Bozenta, for what right had her husband to claim anything more than a formal tie with her? He, by slow degrees, had become a stranger to her. Their differences had occasioned too many quarrels, and their quarreling had increased the sense of difference. She had found him too calculating, too repressed, too much the victim of his own upbringing. She felt that he had loved the *idea* of what she was, rather than herself. He had fallen in love with a picture of her. He had no appreciation and no understanding of the deeper desires of her heart. Her sudden moves, her quick intuitions, her inspirations, so natural to a creature artist—all the things that threw Henryk into raptures of delight—were incomprehensible to Bozenta. He looked upon them as erratic displays of an extravagant personality, and he was acutely irritated by them.

Just what was there between her husband and herself to feed the first fire of attraction into a lasting love? When she dared think of it at all, Helena's conclusion was that she would have done better to have met the other first—the ardent young writer, Henryk Sienkiewicz, six years younger than herself. Yet could she live on regrets all her life? It made her restless to think of Henryk at all.

One morning soon after the departure to the fields of Bozenta, Rudolph, Sypniewski, and the children, Helena was surprised to see Paprocki at the door, looking a little worried. It was not too serious, he said, but Henryk was complaining about feeling ill. He, Paprocki, was going on to the orchard, but perhaps Helena should tend to Henryk.

Helena rushed out of the house in strange alarm. Her hair was still not up, and she hadn't had time to put on her shoes. She seemed to be watching herself as in a dream, knowing that there was no need to become so wildly distraught over a mild sickness, and yet unable to prevent a sense of foreboding. The sun had risen, and the brightness of it blinded her so that she entered the shed barely able to see. She was calling Henryk's name, like one in distress. He answered her from within. A hand caught her by the arm and drew her in, closing the door. It was Henryk. He was up and dressed, murmuring, "Helena, Helena," softly, strangely. Was he really sick? He drew her into his arms, and before she could reason the situation out, she was clinging to him, as he plied her face, her hair, her neck, with impassioned kisses. She could find neither the strength nor the desire to tear herself away. Too long, for so ardent a nature, had she suppressed such emotions as she felt now. She knew that Henryk had no inhibitions, no restraints, no moralistic scruples to hold him back, yet she did nothing to fend him off. In fact, her body shook with desire at his touch, and in her confused mind she wondered at how much he had come to mean to her. In a moment of supreme ecstasy she found herself dreaming of Igo, as if . . . as if. . . .

At last he was sitting up and talking to her, one arm like an arch over her body as she lay on the straw bed where Henryk slept at night.

"Helena," he was saying, "throw all this away. Throw him off. Have done with this role you are playing here in Anaheim. Take your son and go to New York. I will meet you there, and we will go back to Europe—together."

Helena put her hand up and stroked his cheek. Henryk's expression was so sad. He always looked sad. It was his eyes that gave him such life, such vitality. She smiled a little, and spoke as if her whole mood were one of compassion and resignation.

"But how is that possible? I have no money, Henryk. And you have none. How would we live?"

"I'll make money with my writing. Leave that to me."

"You know it isn't that easy."

"It'll work out somehow, I tell you. Look, I have finished the novel. I'll publish it in Poland and in several other countries, translated. You'll see. We'll live in Switzerland."

"But what about my career?"

Henryk's melancholy features became fierce with a frown. Helena was always changeable and unexpected in the things she spoke of. She tantalized.

"What about America?" she went on. "I could tour here and make a lot of money."

"So can you in Europe. Come with me, Helena. Live with me. I'll inspire you as no man has ever yet done. You'll act all the great roles like a genius, and I'll write. And we'll be happy."

She sat up, the warm glance of her large, deep eyes embracing him. "These are dreams, Henryk . . . so wonderful, but. . . ."

He got up and started to pace the floor, wildly. He turned to her, his face flushed. She had never seen him so worked up. But the flood of protesting words did not come. The door had opened with sudden violence. Bozenta stood there with Paprocki behind him.

"What is happening here?" cried the Count, and Helena caught the cold menace in his voice. Before she could reply, make some excuse, find some way to protect Henryk from her husband, the latter turned on Henryk with hysterical violence. "But I see. Fornicating with my wife out in the shed, like a peasant with a bare-foot whore! Out of my house! Disgusting! I should have known you had no honor! No honesty! Get out!"

Henryk stood there as if tongue-tied, his face white with passion. The Count reached out a hand to drag him out, but a gesture from Henryk threw him off. They grappled with each other. A brutal hatred blinding them both to any desire but to do the other bodily harm. Helena cried out, struggling to her feet. Paprocki hurled himself between them, and was struck in the face. Slowly the grappling men came to their senses, and sought to cover their quick feeling of shame with violent, bitter words.

Bozenta was the first to control himself. He glanced in abrupt silence at Helena, then turned on his heel and walked out. Paprocki, embarrassed, his eyes lowered, followed suit. Helena was in tears, with hardly the strength to stand. She made a meaningless gesture of her hand to Henryk, and spoke in barely discernible words. *"Badz zdrow,* God be with you, Henryk. Remember me."* And she moved out into the glaring sun.

Helena was his first and great love. That was how Henryk saw it. But she would not go with him. He was never seen in Anaheim after that day. He left without saying goodbye to anyone. He was destined to fame in his writings, with his *Trilogy, The Knights of the Cross,* and his *Quo Vadis?* But he never forgot Helena, and repeatedly found her in the romantic women of his stories.

There was little time for thought or rest at the farm in Anaheim after Henryk's departure, for soon the oranges and grapes would ripen. The harvest would be unusually good. Baskets and crates had to be ready. Contracts with the buyers from the larger cities had to be settled. It looked as though the work put into the farm would pay off. And yet a certain bright enthusiasm had gone from all of them. The work was arduous. They were constantly caught up in disagreements over petty problems.

As for Helena, she was again withdrawn and depressed. The recitations and the songs had ceased.

19. THE HARD WAY

SYPNIEWSKI HAD the pleasure of seeing his wife get well. She began to take over her share of the work around the house. In fact more than her share, and it was fortunate, as Helena's energies along this line had noticeably flagged. The spirit had gone out of her. She would go into the same brooding silences that had marked her journey to America. She would shut herself in her room, or go for long walks alone. She hardly spoke more than two words at a time to anyone now. Her friends began to grumble. She was spoiling the whole venture she had started against so much opposition from her husband. They began to sympathize with Bozenta when he flew into his rages over trifling matters. The quarrels in the house seemed incessant. These scenes would always end in Helena throwing out some short, sharp retort and retreating to her room. But as far as anyone could see, Helena was making not the slightest effort to set things right again.

The return on the fruit crop had not been what was expected. Bozenta was now moaning that he had lost fifteen thousand dollars because of her, and that they had got nothing out of it but a lot of hard toil. Sypniewski, who at other times had some calming influence over the man, found now that he could say nothing of encouragement. He and Paprocki agreed that the Count was more like his own self at those times when they could drag him away from Helena's presence altogether. But at the sight of her approaching, he would grow tense and dark with bitterness, ready at the slightest opportunity to find fault with her.

As it happened there were others in California who were not unmindful of how a great artist was allowing her talents to waste away on a farm. On a quiet fall afternoon, when the men had come in from the fields, and the family was sitting down to their midday meal, there came the sound of carriage wheels up the driveway. Helena, who went to the door, was surprised to see the theatrical producer Henry Sargent. That wise and canny man of business was heading a delegation of fans. With him were the actress, Miss Rose Eytinge, the well-known actor, Joseph Jefferson, and the grand old man, John McCullough. Helena invited them to join in the Polish meal and to drink Polish vodka.

During the polite conversation that began their meeting, Helena watched her guests curiously. She was more than impressed by such a distinguished array of theatre people, but she could not imagine why they had come to her in this way. There was obviously something in the wind, and Henry Sargent was the ringleader. Yet they were beginning very cautiously. Henry Sargent himself said very little, although his features were fixed in an affable expression.

It was after the first glass of vodka that McCullough began. Helena prepared herself. She could see by the way he was doing it that he had been appointed to fire the opening gun. He began by speaking of the memoirs he was engaged in writing. He was very charming and fatherly, as she remembered him. Then he turned to her, asking her a direct question. "There was that incident between you and my old helper, Mr. Barton Hill. I wanted to put that in my memoirs, but my old head has forgotten the details. Could you tell me about it?"

Helena went off into a fit of laughter that almost shocked her Polish household. She had not laughed like that since Henryk's departure. Her guests stared at her, astonished.

There was a twinkle in her eyes as she turned to McCullough. "Is this the only reason why you came here then?"

The whole delegation grinned. Old John looked somewhat embarrassed, but Jefferson's round, fat face creased with a foxy smile that betrayed the whole row of his spoiled teeth. "No, that is not the only reason."

"Well," said Helena without further questioning, "he was very kind, M-e-e-s-t-e-r Hill, but he was nervous and fussy, and he patronized me, as though I were a child, a little girl. As you know, it was my second experience with him. 'Now,' he said to me, 'I shall be very cri-ti-cal, ve-ery severe.' But I'm afraid I couldn't find it in me to be patient any longer. And I burst out with—'Be as critical and severe as you like, only do please be quiet and let us begin.' He was so taken aback by my words that he could not speak, and I began at once to do a scene from *Adrienne*. I played it through and then I turned to him. He had his handkerchief in his hand. There were tears in his eyes. He came up to me and took my hand. He seemed quite calm, and I asked him, 'Well, do I have that evening that I want?' He told me he would give me a week and more if he could possibly do it. That's the story, John."

From then on conversation grew lively. Everyone wanted to tell some incident in his own theatrical career, and Miss Eytinge wanted to know how Helena approached her new roles.

"I can never understand a part," she spoke up immediately, "unless I can see the character in front of my eyes. The idea in my mind must stand out before me. I must see it clearly. Look at it. Shall I say it must be an impersonation? A presence? And unless I can see it like that, I will not be able to do it. A character must present itself before me before I understand it. And when it fails to do that, then I wait."

That pleased her fellow actors immensely. Helena was beginning to enjoy herself. She forgot the morose presence of her husband.

Miss Eytinge was speaking of the nights when one gives a perfect performance, when the spell over the audience is complete and superb. "Why should this be only on certain nights? Do you know why?" she asked Helena.

"Never," Helena answered. "For example, I have been ill and I play better than ever before. Then I have been ill and not played well at all. It's the same as when I am well. I cannot say I played well because I felt well or ill or happy or anxious or dissatisfied. It's a combination of subtle elements, I suppose. They unite to produce that indefinable thing—success. But I can't grasp it. I can't tell what it is. Perhaps because it is a spiritual condition."

"Ah," exlaimed Mr. Jefferson delightedly, "I have what I call my 'demon,' you see. And if my 'demon' is not with me I cannot play well."

Helena laughed. "I call mine 'my angel.'"

"That is flattering the gods, my dear," said old John, patting her hand.

It was agreed that the guests should stay for dinner. Bozenta made his excuses and left for the fields with his helpers. It brought Helena back to wondering why she had been blessed by this sudden visit. Surely it must be a most important occasion to bring so illustrious a band to Anaheim. Vodka was brought out under the shade of a tree, and they sat there, talking most animately, when at least the reason came out.

This time it was Mr. Jefferson who had been selected for the role. Helena guessed it when he leaned forward in his chair, held his hand before him in a grand gesture, and spoke in well-modulated tones.

"Too bad that Madame Modjeska has forsaken her theatre. A farm? Anyone can work on a farm. But for a genius of the stage. . . . Ah!" His ending sigh was far more affecting than a multitude of words.

Mr. Sargent nodded his head quickly in agreement. "Yes, yes. In the history of the theatre it is only once in a hundred years that an artist can give a performance as great as yours."

Helena smiled, flushed a little, and thanked them for the compliment. But they would not have done. They had come for this purpose. They were prepared to stay there making an impressive nuisance of themselves until Madame Modjeska had agreed to end this nonsensical puttering on a farm.

That evening she signed a contract with Henry Sargent for a two-year tour of the United States and Canada. Everyone was pleased. Her husand was gratified because now at last their finances would be straightened out. Her Polish friends were relieved because now they would have a period of peace on the farm. The Count could be pleasant enough with them. He was kind to them and amenable to their suggestions. Without the constant need of finding fault with Helena, he would return to his normal and charming self. Helena was pleased, because she would now be quit of him and back in the theatre once more.

Her first appearance in New York took place at the Fifth Avenue Theatre, December, 1877, in the play *Adrienne Lecouvreur*. It was a most distinguished audience that came to see the Polish actress, and a most enthusiastic one. The critics raved about her talents and society took her up. She played Juliet, Marguerite, Peg Woffington, and also the leading roles in *Frou-Frou* and *East Lynne*. She was called a genius by such an eminent critic as William Winter of the *New York Tribune*. Richard Watson Gilder, editor of *The Century*, and his sister Jeannette, the writer, came to be numbered among Helena's best friends. The fact was that Helena Modjeska had managed to stir the imagination of many a creative artist, eager to be her friend. In a letter to Brander Matthews, concerning her performance in *Camille*, George H. Jessop quoted Beethoven's remark about the opening chords of the *Fifth Symphony*, "Fate knocks at the door," for he saw the imminence of fate in Modjeska's playing of the role, which, he said, gave the play the power of the old Greek tragedies.

All this acclaim and devotion from the critics and the artists, those who led the fashions of the people, was precious to Helena, for in some way it made up for the emptiness she felt in her private life. Only her most intimate friends could know of her inward sufferings. Her troubled, sleepless nights were haunted by visions and scenes from plays that leaped out before her tired eyes, and at these times she would think she say Igo's pale, intense face float before her as on the cold bluish-green Vistula.

Helena needed someone to whom she could unburden her imaginary sufferings. Edwin Booth saw much of her in New York and began to sense the unhappiness that seethed inside her. He felt an earnest desire to be of some help to her, but his own position was not easy. Some nine years before, he had married his second wife, a Shakespearean actress, Mary McVicker, and she had grown cruelly jealous of Edwin's every natural gesture of friendship to any other woman. To divert his wife's attention and occupy her mind with something more worthy of her talents, he bought a theatre, which he named after himself, and presented to her. His idea was that she should assume the administration of the theatre and make a name for herself as manager as well as actress, but she began to complain that her friends were undermining her artistic career by putting too much emphasis on her business ability. She was an actress of some stature and she desired to be thought of as such.

As a result of this attitude, the Booth Theatre was disastrously mismanaged. Edwin sank more money in the venture than he could afford and was facing bankruptcy. Something drastic had to be done. His fellow actors wanted to help him. It was suggested that he join with Modjeska in a series of Shakespearean plays and play at the Booth Theatre. Alexander Salvini and Lawrence Barett gave him the financial help he needed for this project.

So Helena found herself playing Juliet to Edwin's Romeo before a house packed with cheering people. New York went wild. The two actors were feted wherever they went and were invited to all the social centers. Helena charmed everyone with her talk, her lively wit, and her fondness for a deep discussion. Sometimes she would go to the piano and play or sing her Polish songs.

The poetess Celia Thaxter composed a sonnet in Helena's honor:

Deft hands called Chopin's music from the keys.
Silent she sat, her slender figure's poise
Flower-like and fine and full of lofty ease;
She heard her Poland's most consummate voice
From power to pathos falter, sink and change;
The music of her land, the wond'rous, high,
Utmost expression of its genius strange,—
Incarnate sadness breathed in melody.
Silent and thrilled she sat, her lovely face
Flushing and paling like a delicate rose
Shaked by summer winds for its repose
Softly this way and that, with tender grace,
Now touched by sun, now into shadow turned,—
While bright with kindred fire her deep eyes burned!

Mary McVicker listened to all the inevitable gossip about the close friendship between this magnificent pair of actors, and she was consumed with envy and jealousy. She berated Edwin constantly for his behavior toward Helena, and created scenes in the houses to which Helena and the Booths were invited. She went so far as to bribe one of Helena's maids to let her into the actress' apartment. When Helena returned from the theatre that night it was to find Edwin's wife hiding behind the door. A violent clash of words ensued, in which Mary accused Helena of having intimate relations with her husband. They quickly exhausted themselves emotionally. Helena began to perceive in all this that Mary's tragic need of love was a condition very close to her own. She was able to get her to sit down with some degree of calm, and they talked far into the night. With understanding grew friendship. Mary was completely reassured. Conscious-stricken at what she had done, she took Helena's maid into her own house so that no one would have to suffer for her deed.

From this time on, Edwin was amazed to see with what pleasure his wife collected the clippings which praised the performances he was giving with Modjeska. If Mary and Helena disputed over anything at all, it was on the matter of acting itself. When the most severe and most important critic in New York, William Winter, wrote in the *Tribune* that the acting of Modjeska "taught again the old and precious lesson that poetry is not a dream," Mary McVicker accused Helena of bewitching the old critic with her physical charms. It seemed that she could not understand the greatness of her friend's acting, and her earnest study and devotion to her art. None could have answered Mary better than by quoting Charles E. L. Wingate, writer and critic, who tried to analyze Modjeska's accomplishment:

Although the personality of Madame Modjeska is charming, with her graceful figure, her beautiful face and her sweetly modulated voice, yet this is not the attribute to which her success is due. The auditor has been drawn by that magnetism which comes from warm enthusiastic absorption in the character of the moment, and from the consequent natural expression of all the passions of a woman's heart. Coldly studying the role of the night, one feels that each movement and inflection has been planned with the mind of a careful student; but, even as he watches, his enforced coldness must disappear, and the subsequent warmth of sympathy conceals the conscientious actress, and reveals only the fictional woman, with all sorrows and joys, loves and hates.

Helena went on tour with Edwin, traveling through the major cities. Never before had such respect and veneration been given to an actress from abroad. She was soon being honored by the title of "Grande Dame" of the theatre. Though humbly pleased by this show of admiration, Helena enjoyed her busy life too well for any display of that "pomposity" she so dis-

liked in some celebrities. She never lost her strong sense of fun.
She loved to tell jokes on herself, particularly those untoward
things that had happened on the stage.

There was the first time she played Adrienne at the Fifth
Avenue Theatre and during the entire first act was holding a
shoehorn in her hand instead of her fan. Helena had two Siamese cats, Maciek and Tacik, that were kept in her dressing
room during the performance. At one time, when she was playing Ophelia, these two slipped out of the dressing room and
during a climactic moment in the play came on the stage to steal
the scene. The situation was only saved by Helena covering
them with her long white dress, where they remained from view
of the audience until the curtain fell to the sound of riotous
applause.

This incident was talked about so much that the publicity
agents decided to exploit the subject. They reasoned that everyone likes animal stories, especially when connected with prominent artists. From this time on much prominence was given to
Helena's liking for pets of all kinds.

When she was acting in Louisville, Kentucky, Henry Watterson gave Helena a present of a poodle named Conrad. The manager wanted to make the most of this, and arranged that
"Marse" Watterson should present the dog to Helena on stage
at the end of the play. The dog was dressed up for the occasion
with an elaborate red and gold collar. A speech was made by the
donor, and to everyone's great delight they saw the great Modjeska clasp the woolly beast to her breast and kiss it on the
head. The local press played it up to the full, and the story was
picked up by other papers, until it spread across the country.

The next night, Helena played in *Adrienne Lecouvreur*. During the last act, when she was writhing under the baleful influence of the poison bouquet, Conrad calmly walked onto the
stage. By some chance he had broken free of his leash. He recognized his mistress, sat in the middle of the stage and seemed
to be studying her in astonishment. Behind the scenes, the stagehands were coaxing in loud whispers and with frantic gestures,
but Conrad was too engrossed in the play. He ignored everything but his mistress, who was trying her best to shoo him off
in a way that would not be too noticeable to the audience. But

such a hope was vain. The audience had a grand time, as they watched that comical poodle walking up and down the stage, gazing and sniffing, in the most tragic moments of the play. The tragic effect of the scene was completely ruined, but the public enjoyed itself hugely.

As the curtain was coming down, the stagehands rushed to grab Conrad. But Conrad had his own ideas. He leaped out into the auditorium, bounded up the aisle, and darted into the street. There were screams of laughter and pandemonium in the audience, as everyone joined in the chase of this ungrateful beast.

20. EDWIN AND I

AN ACTOR who has learned to express all the subtleties of human nature should have a vast understanding of human beings and possess a true nobility of soul. Helena mourned the fact that this was so often not the case with actors who had climbed to the position of stars. But in Edwin Booth, Helena decided she had found a man who possessed this nobility of soul as a quality born in him.

While on tour with Booth in 1889–90, she began to make notes in the form of a diary, which she called "Our Life in a Private Railroad Car."

Milwaukee, April 22:

We played *Hamlet* last night. . . .
The audience was cold and unsympathetic.
After the performance we went to the car and had supper. Edwin Booth was delightful. He told us some of his early experiences: how in Honolulu he was compelled to paste his own bills on the corners of the streets, and was surprised at that work by a fellow from New York who happened to be there just at that time. This happened, of course, some years ago. . . .
I went to bed directly after supper, but I heard him talking to the ladies of the company for more than an hour. They all shrieked with laughter.

Cedar Rapids, April 23:

We arrived about 1 P.M. After breakfast went for a stroll. It was a bright sunny day. Felt as though let out of school. I found Cedar Rapids just an ordinary country town, peaceful and dull. At dinner Edwin told us more stories about himself. He talks well. In fact, when he gets going, he is superb.
Edwin sits at the head of the table. . . . Opposite him there is nothing but a mirror, so that he doesn't have to look at anyone but himsel. But I am sure this was not purposely arranged.

167

I am still reading the letters of Wagner and Liszt. I keep remembering the phrase: "Do something new, new, always new." And I long to find some new roles to play.

Edwin is just taking his afternoon nap, and in my stateroom I can hear his steady sonorous breathing, that is called "snoring." As I sit here, it makes me think how treacherous our earthly blessings are. But I do not wish to become depressed just because some of the best people cannot prevent themselves from snoring.

The day is so lovely. The birds are singing, and the chickens make quite a pretty row upon the fence.

Sophie just told me in secret that—but secrets are secrets, and I am not going to gossip. "This is spring, my child," I said, "and Nature is responsible for it."

"Oh! oh! oh!" I exclaimed, and put my handkerchief to my nose when we passed the threshold of the Cedar Rapids temple of art. I wonder if there is any part of Hades that smells as bad. Later, we found out that a tannery stood just behind the theatre. We burned pastilles, Chinese sticks, paper, and a lot of cotton trying to drown out that awful odor. And I sprinkled the stage with *eau de Cologne,* and kept my bottle to my nose for the entire performance. And still during the court scene I felt quite sick.

How I wish some of the stage-struck girls could have been here last night, that I could give them the pleasure of smelling the stage, which, in their imagination, is a heavenly ground strewn with roses. If any of them could see the dressing-room poor Portia occupied, they would slink away from this deceitful Paradise, and thank Heaven and their good parents for a comfortable home. . . .

Last night, we had a very interesting conversation about London and Henry Irving. We both agreed that Irving is a great man. Edwin said, "He's not a great actor, but he is a great man. His knowledge of human nature and his fibs are equally great."

Tried to get Edwin to come for an outing, but he refused. The fact is he never goes out. All exercise tires him and leaves him unfit for the evening's work. I noticed that his left arm is a trifle stiff. He showed me where it was broken. It happened when he fell from a dog cart, and it never healed properly.

Davenport, April 24:

Another uninteresting town. And dirty. While walking, met some of the members of the company. The spring—oh, how treacherous it is!

Peoria, April 25:

Another town of little interest. We took our customary walk, strolling about and pausing before the store windows. There were posters up of Madame Janauschek. What a powerfully expressive face! And what a genius! I wish I had half her talent.

At dinner, or rather after it, Edwin entertained me again with his talk.

He said he has no ear for music. But if anyone makes a mistake when reciting blank verse he finds it immediately jars upon him like a false note. Of course he is very particular about pronunciation, correct emphasis, and voice inflection. And he was kind enough to point out some of my own mistakes. I thanked him and tried to remember what he said for when I give my next performance of Lady Macbeth. For his remarks were all to do with that particular part.

In the *Merchant of Venice,* he told me at first he did not like my putting my hand on Shylock's arm in the "mercy speech," but after more thought about it he had come to the conclusion that it was well worked out, and in fact "a beautiful piece of business." He also praised my delivery of the "mercy speech" as excellent. I was pleased with his praise, and moved by his sincerity.

It seems that the reason why he has not studied any new parts for a long time is that, whenever he put a new play on the bills, the audience kept away from it and asked for *Hamlet, Richelieu,* etc.—plays which he has played for years. It is a very strange thing that people should be so conservative in their taste, but it is certainly the case with Americans, and the older the play the better "the draw."

He played *Richard III,* studied *King John,* played Cardinal Wolsey in *Henry VIII,* and some other parts, but without success; not because they were criticized, but because the people liked the old favorites better.

Decatur, April 26:

Hamlet on the bills.

The weather dreadful. Everything looked bleak and dirty. The view from the train depressing enough to make one despair. Even the pigs, slopping around in the cold mud, looked as if they were sulking.

Edwin played Hamlet gloriously. I was entranced as I watched from the wings. His performance acted as a challenge to me, and I played Ophelia better than ever. I caught sight of Mrs. E.'s pale face watching me intently through the play. She has just lost her father. A curious feeling of tenderness took hold of me while singing: "White his shroud as the mountain snow." And tears came to my eyes, as I sensed her gazing at me from her box. Never have I understood so well that phrase of Liszt: "Reason tells us that we must become wise through feeling." So it is. Only through feeling do we arrive at the truth of things!

After the performance we were, as usual, chatting about various things, when the talk again turned to "shop." Edwin described Charlotte Cushman as being truly beautiful when she was old. Her features softened with age, and her constant suffering gave her face a look of exaltation that she never possessed in her youth. She used to imitate all Macready's mannerisms, even to his way of speaking; having played with him for years, she got into the habit of echoing him without being conscious of it. Forrest dubbed her "Macready in petticoats," and she called him a brute, and they loathed each other heartily.

April 27:

Today was Sunday. The birds woke me up. It was a grand morning. There was something solemn and yet sweet and touching in this awakening of a spring day. The air had the same fragrance it has in Poland. . . . I yearned for the chance to visit Poland with the same intense eagerness as a child yearning for the sight of his mother—and I dreaded it also. Will my friends be the same to me as before? I have not written to anyone there since I left the country. . . . They have a right to be angry with me.

Shall I play in Warsaw, and how will the audiences like me after all these years? When I last appeared before them I was still called "the bewitching Madame Helena."

I know I have not lost my powers, and my talent is now in its full vigor, but I fear the people will look for wrinkles on my face, and, what is worse, they will find them. The wrinkles on a woman's face are a marvelous cooling agent in the stream of enthusiasm, although those on my own do not show on the stage, being not very numerous or very deep; yet I am afraid of the critical eyes of my countrymen. . . .

Coming home, we found Edwin smoking his cigar in the observation room. He opened the door, and said "Tickets," imitating the conductor. Then, of course, we all laughed and chatted until dinnertime. After dinner Mr. and Mrs. E. took us for a drive and then to their home.

A country house is always attractive to me, and I spent my afternoon in the atmosphere of goodness, hospitality, and provincial *naïveté* which is so delightful in small doses. And then the children were so pretty. What did we talk about? Everything and nothing.

It was almost eight o'clock before we got home, I mean got back to the private car. The car's name is *Hazlemere*. Edwin did not go out at all. I fear his health is failing rapidly. Nevertheless he is in excellent spirits and we sat talking until two o'clock in the morning. How many things he remembers! It would be impossible to put down all I heard that evening; but I remember that we talked of spiritualism, art, and travel, and also a little bit about actors. I say *we* talked. I should say *he* talked. I only listened and marveled at Edwin's narrative gift, his impressionability, and intelligence. Those who do not know him cannot nearly imagine what he is like. Very often I hear people say: "He is getting old—he never talks," or, "Is he interesting in private? Is his conversation original?" Those are the individuals who do not know him sufficiently. His chief fault is indolence, and also what his father described as a "bump of I-don't-care-a-damnativeness." He loathes doing things for show, and the result is that when he is with people, it is only when he has confidence in them that he opens the valve of his eloquence. Then he is magnificent.

Bloomington, April 28:

Macbeth.

Another odd little town. An uneventful day. I took my customary walk, and purchased some flowers to decorate the dining table. After dinner I wrote letters, and at seven set off for
the theatre. What a quaint little stage! My dressing room was
painted vermillion, and made my eyes ache. Everything about
the place was shabby and commonplace, even to the scribblings
on the manager's notice that usually hangs in each dressing
room. The scribbled remarks were in pencil, evidently written by
some frustrated actor, and I am sorry to say they were obscene.

Otis Skinner as Macduff went on without fleshings last night.
He streaked his legs with red and brown and magenta to look
like the cuts and wounds that Macduff received in battle. It
was most effective.

Indianapolis, April 29:

Arrived at 2 P.M.

We played *Macbeth* again, and this time Vroom and Hanley
joined Otis Skinner in the bare leg display. Skinner and Vroom
painted their legs so that they looked natural, but Hanley did
not, and his plump white columns looked out of place. The cool
night made them all shiver, but they were full of pride in their
looks. The following morning there was a statement in the
paper: "Macduff, Malcolm, and Ross were more realistic than
effective. A little less meat and a little more dressing would have
been not only more artistic but more satisfying."

Vincennes, April 30:

We played *Hamlet*. Small town managers seem to have a
mania for signs. This time they appeared in the tin trough that
serves as the reflector for the footlights. As soon as Edwin
came off stage after his first scene, he said to me, "Take a look
at the signs in the footlights." Otis Skinner, who was playing
Laertes, and myself were just going on, and I nearly laughed
out loud when I saw a sign reading: "Do not spit in this
trough." It appeared three times, once on each end of the footlights and once in the middle. It at once became the subject for

all the evening's jokes. When Ben Rogers (Polonius) had finished his words of counsel to Laertes, he added in an undertone: "And do not spit in this trough."

What a nice old man Ben is. It is a real pleasure to talk to him behind the scenes. He is always cheerful and contented. I never once heard him griping or protesting. Even when the company has got up at five in the morning to catch a train, and when everyone else looks haggard and tired in the evening, he is full of smiles and is as gay as ever. Once I asked him if the traveling did not tire him. "What!" he cried, "A young man like me tired? Never!" He is over seventy. He is not only a wonderful person, but also a really good comedian. His acting of the father in *Garrick,* his Gobbo, Polonius, and Dogberry are perfect.

At supper Edwin was not feeling well, but still he was very entertaining. He told us that once his brother Junius, who was a manager at that time, wanted him to play a part which was supposed to have been written especially to suit all his talents, a part in which he had to play the fiddle, sing, and dance. It seems, however, that the musical and terpsichorean capability of our tragedian did not inspire him with sufficient confidence to produce them before the public. Therefore fiddle, song, and dance were cast out of the part. He said also that most of the time in his early days he played comedy.

We had a special train. The ladies were invited to the car. After supper Edwin went to the observation room to smoke his cigar. There he found the ladies. Also Mr. Smith, who is given the same privilege being the husband of Mrs. Smith; Otis Skinner, because he is one of the featured players; and Ben Rogers, because of his age.

The train was rattling along, making a great noise. We chatted away about the performance of the night before, about the flowers Miss Proctor had picked from the fields, about clothes, and costumes, and other significant things. Edwin was talking to someone a little distance from me, so that I could not hear what he was saying, but I followed the movement of his hands, and nearly understood what he had said. His hands and his eyes are remarkably expressive. He was describing some Indians and the way they shoot, and I could see the arrows fly in the air and the savage faces of the Indians. When the noise lessened, I heard him giving a very graphic description of his visit to the Mammoth Cave in Kentucky. He never says too much or too little, and that's what makes everything he says so interesting. I think that this is characteristic, even in his acting —that he always finds a right measure. Even when situations might tempt him to exaggerate, he very seldom oversteps the limits. There may be an exception in one or two instances in *Richelieu,* but in Shakespeare—never. Sometimes he gives too little rather than too much, but for that only the state of his health is responsible. He often is tired and ill. I heard him saying after some scene, "I wish I had all my strength and vigor to play this as I ought to play it."

Louisville, May 1:

We left the car and stayed at a hotel that night. When I got to the theatre, I found my dressing room gloriously decorated. There was an enchanting red glow from the electric light on the table, and the walls were draped with wild flowers and ivy. This was done on the occasion of the first day of May at Miss Proctor's suggestion. She and four or five young people went to the woods and brought back almost a carload of flowers and other greens, and they decorated Edwin's room and mine. Miss Proctor is always thinking up such rare touches, and she has a passionate love of flowers. I used to hand my flowers over to her and often wondered how she kept them fresh so long. It is the loving way she cares for them that keeps them alive.

May 2:

We played *Macbeth,* and I discussed with Edwin the question of cuts. We both were in agreement that my banquet scene beginning, "Oh, proper stuff!" seemed too long, and that it would be better to shorten it.

Now it goes:

> Oh, proper stuff!
> This is the very painting of your fear. . . .
> Shame itself!
> Why do you make such faces? When all's done,
> You look but on a stool.

Also in the speech before it:

> Sit, worthy friends: my lord is often thus,
> And hath been from his youth. . . .
> Feed, and regard him not.

May 3:

Hamlet, matinee; *Merchant of Venice* at night.

The performance of *Merchant of Venice* lasted until midnight. I thought that half the audience would leave, but they stayed until the last moment. When we came home it was nearly 1 A.M.

On the road, May 4, Sunday:

We have changed our car. This one is called *Newport.* It is not as pretty or comfortable as *Hazlemere,* and not as clean since it is old. We spent the whole day sitting in the observation room—talking and reading. When it grew dark, I sat on the platform.

Edwin looks pale and worn. He tried to read by the dim light of the car lamps. I went to my room, brought two candles, and set them up on the sofa at his elbow. He turned, and with an angelic smile said, "How kind you are!" in a tone which might have been interpreted as an expression of surprise.

After this he resumed his reading, and I went back to the platform to spin a thread of thoughts flying toward the Atlantic. . . .

How often in the past did I sit, on such an evening, dreaming of fame! And how different my dreams are now. Better to have no fame; rather a home full of love. The long winter evenings of my youth come to mind, with all their warmth. Mother sat at the table with her work and we sat around, one of us reading aloud and the rest busy with drawing or sewing. Anything. How far those evenings are from me now!

Dayton, May 5:

I spent the day in my room.

We played *Merchant of Venice,* and after the play, while at supper, we talked about trees and rivers. I spoke of the date palms I had seen in Los Angeles, a male and a female. They

were both very tall, but the male was much taller, and they
seemed like a pair of lovers, with the smaller one almost clinging to the other. It seems that people have a certain respect for
them, for even though there is a building craze going on now,
with trees being chopped down all around, these two are left
untouched. Edwin said: "I think trees have feeling. I do not
know what religion I have, but I believe trees love us when
we treat them kindly. Why should we have so much affection
for them, if they do not reciprocate in some unfelt and unseen
way? I planted a grove of trees on my grounds once. I sold the
place long ago, but I never go to New York without stepping
on the platform to look at them. They are as dear to me as
children."

Zanesville, May 6:

Arrived at 3 P.M.

I stayed in bed past noon. I find that the most sensible thing
is to lie down when we are not forced to get up.

We played *Richelieu.*

During the performance we had some amusement. A young
man in our company who plays François was born and brought
up in this town. Previous to our coming, the editor of the local
paper received a notice disparaging the company, but praising
him highly. This notice was repeated in the paper. It is easy to
guess who sent it.

The audience was thus prepared. In the first act while Richelieu was on stage, this young man did not wait for his cue,
but anticipated Edwin's words and walked on with quick steps
and dignified demeanor—a regular star entrance. His friends
in front gave him a round of applause which thoroughly amused
everyone behind the scenes. In the fourth act someone threw a
bouquet to him, which he picked up gracefully, smiling and bowing—"à la Modjeska," someone said behind me.

Edwin was amused, but said he did not like that sort of
thing; usually more harm than good comes of it. He is right.
Our friends are sometimes our worst enemies. This young man
is already frightfully conceited. He exhibits his photograph in
shop windows, flatters the critics to get good notices, and does

many things that would be repulsive to any modest young actor. He may have talent, but he must take time to ripen. Flattery is too often destructive.

Wheeling, May 7:

I read in the paper two or three days ago that there was a fight for tickets in Wheeling; the police interfered, and some people were bruised.

Last night we sat talking a long time after supper. We spoke of Shakespeare, Boucicault, Bacon, and Donnelly. Edwin spoke of how he studies Shakespeare. He says, "It is not enough to take one edition and study your part from it; you have to see as many editions as you can get to find the true meaning of a word sometimes." And then he quoted different readings of different people. It is strange that the most far-fetched meaning is usually the most popular with actors.

We spoke of blank verse and prose, and how difficult it is not to fall into the commonplace when you want to be natural.

Edwin's father was both a splendid reader and a great actor. He had never allowed his son to watch him while he played. Edwin used to go to the theatre with him to help him dress, but he was kept in the dressing room and was expected to learn his lessons. He was all ears though, and did not lose one word of his father's reading nor of the other actors. As a result, while he was very young he formed some theatrical opinions and judgments. His father did not want him to acquire any of his own peculiarities. He used to say: "I want your ear to be educated first."

It seems that Edwin has been three times a star and three times reduced to the position of an ordinary actor in stock companies. His salary, while he was engaged at a Philadelphia theatre, was six dollars a week and after two weeks of trial, he was discharged for incompetency.

Edwin spoke a great deal about the right pronunciation of certain words on the stage. To make the blank verse sound well he changes the inflection of vowels. In *Hamlet* he pronounces "orisons" with the inflection on the letter "i"—orisons, while it ought to be *o*risons, with a short "i" and the inflection on the letter "o." He does it to suit the melody of the blank verse and to avoid the jerky sound which the correct pronunciation would produce.

Wheeling:

Merchant of Venice.

While Edwin was taking his afternoon nap, I sat down to write. Suddenly I heard the voice of our waiter calling the porter to show him the crowd gathered on the shore. (Our car had stopped at the bank of a river.) A few minutes later Mr. Chase, our business manager, came in and told me that a boat had been struck and overturned by a steamer. Twenty people went down—two of them drowned. He said it with such cheerfulness that I thought he was telling me of some advertising trick he had arranged; but I turned to our waiter, and from his expression I understood that it was no trick.

The audience was large and very sympathetic. I began in a splendid mood, but before the third act, Mr. Skinner told me of Charles Vandenhoff's death (the actor who had made such a hit while playing with me in *Les Chouans*). The tragic news spoiled the rest of my performance. My face was wet with tears all through the third act.

Charles Vandenhoff was one who was disliked bitterly by some, but loved dearly by others. He was the best friend I ever had in the profession. It is dreadful to think that he, with all the refinement and delicate tastes he possessed, should die in a hospital in Washington Territory—a half-civilized country where the word "comfort" is almost unknown. Poor dear man! What a generous and grateful nature he had! What pains he had taken to correct my English and instruct me in the meaning of obscure passages in Shakespeare. I did not even write to him lately; it is hard to think of the duties which we have not fulfilled and can no longer fulfil because it is too late.

Our season closed in Buffalo with the *Merchant of Venice*. After the court scene and while we were taking curtain calls, I glanced at my dear Edwin Booth and was struck by the strange feeling that I would never see him again. Tears filled my eyes.

Perhaps he had the same thought, for after the final curtain when he turned to me and said, "Goodbye," I saw that his eyes were moist. He seemed to be weak and tired as he walked to his room. . . .

Goodbye, goodbye. . . .

21. LONGFELLOW IN HER LIFE

Fᴙᴏᴍ ᴘʜɪʟᴀᴅᴇʟᴘʜɪᴀ, Helena Modjeska traveled to Boston to play in the famous Boston Museum. Her renown had preceded her, so that all the notables of the city were present to see her, including Oliver Wendell Holmes, James T. Fields, Thomas Bailey Aldrich, and Henry Wadsworth Longfellow. Longfellow, more than seventy years old at this time, was nearing the end of a long life, but he still possessed a young and romantic heart. He was one of the first of the distinguished group that came to pay respects at Helena's dressing room after the play.

"I have seen many actresses play in *Camille*," he told her, "but you, my dear, are far superior to them all."

Helena was touched by such a compliment and thanked him modestly.

"In the hands of other actresses," he went on, "the play could seem merely an attack on moral standards. But to watch you playing Marguerite is to be able to sense the depth and tragedy of this woman. And the play is redeemed."

Helena thanked him again and turned the conversation to his poetry. She told him that she wanted very much to organize an evening to the reading of his poems. She hoped she could do them justice. "I am very much in love with *Hiawatha*," she assured him. "I think everyone should learn it by heart."

He smiled. "But you don't want to go wasting your time memorizing those things. And don't you speak of *Hiawatha* to me," he added, with a twinkle in his eyes, "or I'll start calling you Mudjikiewis. After all it's so very near the sound of your name, isn't it?" And he laughed outright like a child.

Longfellow and his distinguished friends invited Helena to dine with them, as soon as she was dressed and could leave the theatre.

The following day she visited the Longfellow house in Cambridge, and the two spent the day together. They took a drive, to see the historical spots, and got out to stroll along the quay of famous old Boston harbor.

"Any stretch of water has a profound effect on me," Helena observed, "particularly the sea. It stirs me in a certain mysterious way."

"That's very interesting," said the poet with a smile, "because for me you know water means just simply water."

Helena looked at him a moment. She was getting used to his sense of fun. But she continued, as he had become serious again and was waiting to hear more. "I remember, for instance, the time when I landed at San Francisco, and traveled around to see the sights. But when I came to the shore again, I grew suddenly depressed. The great waters of the Pacific reminded me of our Vistula. And I began to think of all the happy things that had happened to me in the past—Cracow, with its many churches and its monuments, the friends I had there, the theatre where I had my first success, and all the people who were so kind to me when I played for them. Yes, everything was brought back in such a rush of homesickness that I had to go off alone. And I threw myself down on the sand, and I was gripped by violent sobbing. I couldn't stop myself, but cried on until I was exhausted. Then I sat up, stared across the ocean, and the world had become a vast emptiness, so infinitely sad. I could find no pleasure in it."

The poet listened to hear attentively. It was clear to him that she was giving expression to some deep longing in her soul. Had something in the past betrayed her? Had she committed some act she regretted? Given some pain to another—something she longed to eradicate? It would be far better for her to face it than to flee from it. It might serve to free her from some sense of guilt. He advised her to return to Europe as soon as her American engagements had come to a close, to visit her homeland and the place of her birth. Why didn't she plan on a tour through Ireland, London, Spain, France, Germany, and then Poland?

It was a wise suggestion, for her Shakespearean repertoire was great, and there were more than a few who would swear that no other actress, including Francesca Janauschek, Sarah Bernhardt, Ellen Terry, and Fanny Davenport, could equal her in depth of emotion and brilliance of technique. The roles of Beatrice, Cleopatra, Juliet, Imogene, Lady Macbeth, Ophelia, Portia, Rosalind, and Viola were in the minds of Americans forever connected with Modjeska. And this at no expense to Shakespeare, Schiller, Molière, Goethe, Corneille, and a dozen or so other playwrights. Her repertoire consisted of over a hundred and ten parts which she played with equal ease in English, Polish, French, or German. Her memory was so phenomenal that she could memorize whole plays without any trouble, and never forgot what she had learned.

As Helena and Longfellow walked along the Boston docks, she abruptly came to a stop.

"Is something the matter?" Longfellow asked.

"Do you hear those men talking?"

"Yes. They seem to be talking very fast. I don't recognize the language."

"It is Polish," said Helena, her eyes shining.

"It has a beautiful sound," said the poet charmingly.

But Helena shook her head. "No more beautiful than the language of Shakespeare and Longfellow."

"Then it is my turn to thank you, my dear, for putting my name by that of Shakespeare. But tell me, what are those men talking about?"

"You see the one who is doing most of the talking?" said Helena. "It appears he had a friend in the old country, who with a number of other Poles has managed to escape the Czar's oppression by getting passage on a German boat. The boat has just recently come into Boston Harbor."

Helena moved over to the group and spoke in her own tongue. The men were all husky dockhands, but they seemed overwhelmed by her presence. They recognized her immediately. Many times they had seen her pictures in the Polish press that came to them from Chicago. They had followed her triumphs on the stage. Longfellow, as he watched a few paces away, could hear her name being mentioned repeatedly by the men who were constantly bowing to her.

When she rejoined him on their walk, he spoke of the great politeness of the Polish dockmen. Then he asked her to recite something to him in her native tongue.

Without a second thought she began rapidly in rhythmic stanzas, and her companion listened rapturously. When she had finished he asked: "Whose poetry is it? Something of Mickie-wicz?"

"No."

"Whose then?"

"It was merely the Polish alphabet."

Longfellow stared in astonishment, then let out a howl of laughter.

Helena began again, but in English:

> "Often I think of the beautiful town
> That is seated by the sea;
> Often in thought go up and down
> The pleasant streets of that dear old town,
> And my youth comes back to me."

Longfellow grinned, "But that's something of mine! *My Lost Youth.* And you just said that you would like to memorize my poems? You're an incorrigible flirt!"

Helena took the old man's arm, delighted, and she began to recite his *A Psalm of Life:*

> "Tell me not, in mournful numbers,
> Life is but an empty dream!—
> For the soul is dead that slumbers
> And things are not what they seem."

At that the poet could not hold back, and chimed in with the ensuing lines:

> "Life is real! Life is earnest!
> And the grave is not its goal. . . ."

He suddenly stopped, and looked into her young face. Then with a sigh he said softly, "Oh, if only I were thirty years younger. I would carry you away on one of those ships out there —far, far to some fair island where love and youth go on for-ever!"

"I too regret that deeply," she said softly, and they con-tinued to walk in silence.

In 1880, when Helena was acclaimed for her performances in

London, she received a precious letter from Henry Wadsworth Longfellow:

Now I can add my congratulations on your triumphant entry into London. How pleasant it is to be able to say, "I told you so!" And did I not tell you so? Am I not worthy to be counted among the Minor Prophets? I cannot tell you how greatly rejoiced I am at this new success—this new wreath of laurel.

The friendship between this great American poet and the Polish actress continued, although they were never to meet again. Their correspondence shows their firm affection and admiration for each other.

Two years after their meeting, Longfellow died. Helena Modjeska came to his funeral and placed upon his grave a wreath of red and white roses, the colors of her imprisoned motherland.

22. GENIUS IN THE NUDE

HENRY JAMES, the American writer, reported his reactions to a French star whose name began to be heard beyond the confines of Europe. He saw Sarah Bernhardt perform at the Comédie Française, and he wrote:

Sarah? It would require some ingenuity to give an idea of the intensity, the ecstasy, the insanity, as some people would say, of curiosity and enthusiasm provoked by her. She is not to my sense a celebrity because she is an artist. She is a celebrity because, apparently, she desires with an intensity that has rarely been equaled to be one, and because all ends are alike to her. . . . She is an impertinent *Victrix* poised upon a perfect pyramid of ruins.

In 1879, Sarah Bernhardt made a dynamic appearance on the London stage, playing the title role in Racine's *Phèdre* at the Gaiety. From her very first appearance, it was clear that Henry James had been right. She was out to make an impression on the English-speaking world, and she had the power and genius to do it. In fact, she had suddenly loomed up as a star fabulous enough to challenge the position of Modjeska in the United States.

She was four years younger than Helena, being in her middle thirties. She was a mixture of French and Dutch and Jewish, with all the passion, all the stubborn will power and brilliance that such a combination might suggest. She was blessed with a consuming ambition, and a clever sense of publicity. She set out to make herself as talked about as possible. Having quite a talent for art, she exploited that too. She brought with her to London her paintings and sculpture, and exhibited them and sold them at high prices to her enthusiastic followers. On these alone she was able to make some six thousand dollars. She traveled about with a menagerie of strange animals, as Byron had done before her, and it created the same sensational gossip. She went to Liverpool and ostentatiously purchased herself two lions, a wolf, and a dozen chameleons. The fantastic tales that arose in connection with this obsession were carefully spread by herself, for she would repeat the stories with a curious exultation, never denying or substantiating.

Being feted by the celebrities of London, she made a point of being seen with such highly influential personages as Gladstone and Leighton. It was reported that she threw a live cat into the fire because it had scratched her, that she poisoned a monkey which spat at her, and so on. She herself repeated the following stories: "It was told of me that for a shilling I would let anyone see me dressed as a man; that I smoked huge cigars as I leaned on the balcony of my home; that when I performed in one-act plays at the various receptions given in my honor, I took my maid along to play opposite me; that I practiced fencing in my garden dressed as a *pierrot* in white; and when taking boxing lessons I had knocked two teeth out of the mouth of my unfortunate instructor."

No one could say whether these stories were true or false, for everyone felt that Bernhardt was quite capable of doing such things, so eccentric was she in every phase of her life, including affairs of the heart.

There was talk of Sarah coming to the United States. Henry Abbey was right on hand with a contract. As a producer and publicity agent, he was unsurpassed. He knew what he could do with a woman like Bernhardt. And he had not forgotten that Helena Modjeska had turned down his offers. Now he would have the exquisite pleasure of bringing a rival to American shores. Furthermore, he was able to arrange for her debut at the Booth Theatre, and, what is more, Bernhardt would be playing Modjeska's great role, that of Adrienne Lecouvreur. After inevitable success in New York, she would tour the States and Canada.

Abbey was not disappointed this time. Sarah signed the contract and created the usual sensation at her debut. As a result she could not make a move without the press taking immediate notice. Furthermore, her passionate, sensuous playing of Marguerite in Dumas' famous play *La Dame aux Camélias* had the good fortune to be condemned by certain circles as "scandalous." She was parading the sex life of the heroine before the public!

The Roman Catholic Bishop of Montreal denounced Sarah Bernhardt, her whole Company, and French literature in general. It had no noticeable effect on her audiences but to increase them. She played the role sixty-five times to packed houses both in Canada and the United States. When another Bishop, of the Chicago Diocese, started an attack on Bernhardt's Marguerite, Henry Abbey was ready for him. He wrote the worthy man a letter: "Whenever I visit your city I am accustomed to spend four hundred dollars in advertising. But as you have done the advertising for me, I send you two hundred for the benefit of the poor."

Sarah's first tour on this continent in 1881 netted her one hundred and eighty thousand dollars and vast publicity. Nevertheless, she felt that the American public had not yet recognized her for the outstanding actress that she was. In fact, Modjeska continued to reign. The problem was to convince millions that Sarah was the more beautiful and the greater actress of the two. As the first step in her campaign, she hit upon a unique idea—she would convince the women of the theatre, since women are the backbone of publicity.

Marie Colombier was an actress of Bernhardt's Company, and a master of the art of spreading gossip. Sarah pressed her into service. Whereupon stories went the rounds that were distinctly designed to blur the Modjeska effulgence. Further, Sarah proposed a reception, a brilliant affair, to which all the most famous and most influential actresses in New York would be invited. Marie Colombier entered fully into the spirit of the idea, and carried out the plan to a perfection of detail.

According to Marie Colombier's personal account, it happened in New York. Other sources insist on the Clarendon Hotel in London. Be that as it may, not a man was invited to this notable gathering. The vast and imposing room, hung with Bernhardt paintings, was filled with the greatest female acting talent of the day. All were dressed in the most dazzling and daring gowns that fashion could produce, and were burning with diamonds and sapphires and precious ornaments of gold. There existed an electric undercurrent of rivalry that made the conversation brittle and barbed and tense. The guests drank the rarest wines and champagnes, and grew more and more loquacious.

Helena, who of course had been invited, seemed to be the exception, sitting rather quietly and modestly, observing and listening with unassuming candor. Above the din she could hear the booming, somber voice of Francesca Janauschek, that incomparable portrayer of Medea and Gretchen. The beautiful blue-eyed Mary Anderson, born in the United States but of German extraction, was trying in a thin and faltering though melodic German to talk to Madame Janauschek. Helena could hear the intoxicated utterances of Adelaide Ristori, who was then fifty-eight years old. She looked about the room and recognized the seventy-year-old Anne Kemble, last of a great line; sixty-three-year old Helena Faucit; the fascinating Ellen Terry; the luscious Fanny Davenport.

The hostess herself was as exotic as a flame, set off by her long black gown with white organdy pleated collar and cuffs, decorated by a spray of red roses. Her black eyes were gleaming, and her face was lit by a magnificent turbulence and a nervousness she tried to hide with short cascades of laughter. She circulated with panther movements among the groups of guests, patting some on the back and embracing others. Helena watched her as at a play, and was quite fascinated.

As the evening wore on, the copious drinking of wine began to produce its effect. The gossip was sinking increasingly low and rising to heights of gusto. What began as praise of American landscape and way of life ended as lashing criticism of those wealthy Americans who on first meeting looked for—as their right—the immediate key to the actress' bedroom, without sensitivity, without any feeling for the moment most appropriate for emotional interchange. Those men of success whose time was short in love as in business, but who were still full of the pioneer spirit! That night the private lives of famous men and women of the theatre and of the European aristocracy were exposed, dissected, and dragged in the mire. It was an evening set to destroy reputations.

It drew into morning, and was about three when the raised voice of Marie Colombier broke loose over the distinguished drunken heads of the ladies stretched helter-skelter over sofas and chairs:

"I wish to propose a certain experiment."

Marie Colombier was tall and blond. She had a mysterious smile on her full lips. There was immediate interest among the guests, as she continued.

"Let us agree that the most illustrious among us this evening are Madame Modjeska and Mademoiselle Bernhardt."

There was a stir of resentment and disapproval at such an assumption. There were many present who would never admit —at least in public—any actress to be superior to themselves. Marie Colombier hastened to add that she was thinking of the public attitude of the moment. In the eyes of the public, Modjeska and Bernhardt were rivals. Who was the greater of the two? "To solve this problem," Marie Colombier went on, "I would like to submit them to a decisive test. Of course with the agreement of both of them first."

Everyone showed their pleasure, without knowing in the least what was coming. It was taken at first to be some sort of a joke, and it relieved a growing sense of tedium after so much talking, though as yet no one felt like going home.

Marie Colombier held to a very straight face. She had their earnest attention, and she spoke slowly, precisely, selecting her words with great care. "For the complete appraisal of greatness it is necessary to take into consideration the many, so to speak, invisible elements of acting as an art—the beauty of the body, motion, and rhythm—which I would call the secrets of femininity." She studied the faces of her listeners and found them burning with unashamed curiosity. She knew that she could come out with her proposal boldly. "I propose then that the two contestants entirely divest themselves of all concealments in the way of clothes, and in this attire of Eve demonstrate their prowess."

The room was thrown into an uproar, and yet the cries of consternation were drowned out by those who wildly approved of the plan as daring and original. Before any decisive vote could be taken, Sarah Bernhardt sprang up from her chair, her eyes flashing. "I will do it. Of course, I will. Will you, Helena darling? There are no men around, so that does not have to concern us."

Helena found herself the center of attention, and was annoyed by her sudden embarrassment. Her face flushed. Marie Colombier was moving down on her. "So?"

What could she do but accept the challenge, mad as it was? She nodded her head, and murmured, "I will do it, yes."

Marie Colombier turned and spoke above the wave of excited voices. The first move was to select a jury of three. But they must be three whose judgment would be accepted without question. A discussion ensued that grew more and more heated and lasted another half hour. Finally, it was settled that the three judges would be the world-famous older actresses, Janauschek and Ristori, and the youthful, but highly intelligent, Ellen Terry.

Bernhardt behaved as though she were well pleased with the choice. They were close friends of hers, and she knew they admired her work immensely. She would make of this victory an event of world-shaking importance. It would be given out to all the newspapers, and the world would accept the verdict and hail her as the greatest living actress.

It was decided that both Sarah and Helena should play a scene from Alexandre Dumas' *La Dame aux Camélias*. In the nude both would portray the ravishing Marguerite Gauthier of Dumas' most famous play. Each went into separate rooms to prepare themselves for the contest.

After ten minutes, Sarah came out of her room. Her bronzed body glistened with beads of perspiration and gave off enchanting waves of Parisian perfumes. She danced about like some ecstatic nymph, putting into her movements all the litheness of her short body. Her breasts were small and firm, her legs a little too thick for perfect symmetry, yet adding to the sensuous feeling. Then abruptly she checked herself, and rushed with an astonishing wild passion into the love scene with all the experience of a practiced lover. In every movement of her legs and arms, the serpentine inclinations of her torso, in the agitation of her breasts, and in the beautiful, clear French rolling off her lips, there was the expression of a burning sensual love.

This was the Lady of the Camellias, at sight of whom men throughout the theatres of Paris, London, and New York trembled with desire. To watch her like that so carried away, all breath and life and slightest movement united in this powerful hypnotic concentration on a fatal, forbidden love, was to understand the rigid actions of the censors and the horror of the churches. As she danced in, so she danced out. Back to her dressing room, sure of her conquest, sure of her guests as she was always sure of her audiences.

Helena came out. Although four years older than Sarah, she looked strangely younger. She came in quietly, without the dance of her rival, but she looked more the dancer. Her long legs, the paleness of her flesh, the quietness of her movements, the extreme modesty of her expression, which gave her, despite the maturity of her body, a touch of innocence—all contrived to give the impression of some ballerina caught in a dream. She created an immediate feeling of sympathy in her audience.

Many of her fellow actresses that night found themselves marveling at the youth of her body at forty. It was as if she must possess some secret which held her at the enchanting age of twenty. Her body seemed to have the firmness of steel, yet was alive and supple.

Helena measured every French word with a slight melodic accent, rolling it out like a precious stone. Her interpretation of a courtesan fully corresponded to the prototype, who had been Dumas' inspiration. Arsène Houssaye, who had met the girl in Paris, described her as "refined" and "cultivated," one who "spoke of art with such good opinion that Franz Liszt, meeting her in the foyer of the theatre, took her for a princess."

In her rendition Helena put not the slightest emphasis on sex. There was dignity in the self-conscious grace of her body. Her movements were profoundly premeditated. Here in a short scene was a study, a concept of love, a love conceding to no self-imposed or society-imposed restrictions. She seemed to fuse all the poetic and masterly elements of her being in this creation.

There was a wave of approval from her audience as she turned and walked quietly out, with grace, her head high. The judges wrote down their decisions on slips of paper which were dropped into a tin box, to be read aloud at the conclusion of the party.

The tension was broken and all returned to the wine. There was a perfect babble of light conversation. Marie Colombier was again active among the guests, plying them with more food and drink. The two contestants returned, fully dressed, and were applauded noisily.

The first rays of the sun filtered through the windows before the party began breaking up. A vote of thanks was given to Sarah and Marie for a highly original party. The tin box was brought out and the ballots examined. Two for Modjeska, and one for Bernhardt. All attempts to find out who had voted for whom were unsuccessful. The old adage that women cannot keep a secret was flatly disproved.

A few weeks later, Marie Colombier and Sarah Bernhardt parted company, no longer friends. Marie wrote a derogatory biography of Bernhardt, which she called, *Les Memoires de Sarah Barnum.* But even in this book she failed to disclose the secret of the vote.

The book was published and the "divine Sarah" broke into the home of Marie Colombier on the rue St. Honoré in Paris. She accused Marie of spreading vicious gossip about her life, and even charged that, upon the evening of the contest with Modjeska, Marie tampered with the votes. Sarah's rage knew no bounds, and she ended by horsewhipping the frightened Marie in her own home.

23. A PARABOLA OF TEMPERAMENTS

I N THE fall of 1883, after a restful vacation in California, Helena began a memorable tour from San Francisco with her own Company directed by Fred Stinson. The Company included some of the most prominent actors of the day, such as William Owen, the magnificent interpreter of Sir Toby Belch, Charles Vandenhoff, and Maurice Barrymore with his wife Georgie Drew Barrymore.

Among the plays in their repertoire was *Frou-Frou*. Maurice Barrymore played the part of Valreas with great effect. This member of the Barrymore family was not only an actor of extraordinary talent but a matinee idol, who loved the fuss that the women made over him. He was handsome, loquacious, and dressed impeccably. It pleased him to know that he was given the cognomen of "the dandy leading man." Wherever he played, the women in the audience would vie with each other in letting him know their profound admiration, so that when curtain call came he would be swamped with more flowers than he could hold in his arms.

At times white lilies would be found among them. It happened that Helena had a horror of white lilies. She was convinced that they were a harbinger of ill luck and unhappiness. The mere sight of white lilies would bring upon her several days of nervous disorders, and she made Maurice promise that he would never show them to her.

The Barrymores were insistent that their two children, Lionel and Ethel, attend all matinees so that they could get used to the routine of theatre life and be properly steeped in the tradition at an early age. Lionel was only five and his sister one year younger. The two children were adored by most of the Company, particularly by Helena who possessed a deep love for all children due to the tragic loss of her own child, Marylka.

Lionel had an enthusiasm for art and was forever busy painting fantastic ships and derailed trains, but Ethel did her best to distract him. She wanted to play "theatre," and would set up so much protest that he would usually give in. Left to themselves in the dressing rooms, they would imitate the grownups, composing the most outlandish dialogue, and putting on a whole show. For inspiration they would creep up to the wings and listen to the voices on the stage, and then return to the dressing rooms to present their own versions. Lionel would be "Pop" and Ethel would be "Madame." All was not plain sailing, however, for Ethel would frequently run into difficulty pronouncing words. Lionel would easily lose patience with this failing. He would begin correcting her whole sentence structure, which amounted to an attempt to mold her to his own style of playing. But the little girl had an astonishing spirit of her own that would not be dictated to. When the grownups would look in on their "play," seeing Ethel emoting with such fire and abandon, they would invariably predict a great future for her.

When they had enough of their playing, Ethel would pull her brother close to the stage again to look at the acting of Modjeska. There was a special glint in her large eyes as she watched the actress thrilling the audience with her superb passion. A deep understanding seemed to exist between these two; Helena, who saw in the child something of her past, and little Ethel, who was quite lost in admiration of the fine lady who wore the most gorgeous costumes, and held the audience spellbound by walking on the stage.

Whenever she had the chance, Helena would take the two children to some restaurant where they would eat the richest cakes with cream on the top, or take them to her hotel rooms. On these occasions Ethel would be bubbling with things to say, and loved to sit on the lap of her darling Helena. Lionel, on the other hand, was very serious, speaking like an adult and always keeping a respectful distance from a lady, as if he abided by some code. There were occasions, though, when his reserve broke down. The biggest treat for the children was to be invited by Modjeska to a party of *chrusciki,* which Helena's Polish maid knew how to prepare so well. At these times Lionel would forget himself and plow into the mound of these little cakes twisted into unusual shapes and sprinkled with powdered sugar.

One afternoon after a matinee, Maurice Barrymore received his usual amassment of flowers from his female admirers, and these were left temporarily on the stage after the final curtain. Little Ethel saw them there and went over to them. She carefully selected the largest, most glorious specimens—two bunches of white lilies—and proceeded to Helena's dressing room. Helena was appalled. Her face turned white. She uttered a chilly thank you to the astonished child, who was then left standing as the actress descended upon Maurice's dressing room. Helena was in a terrifying rage that would not respond to reason. She screamed at the dismayed and innocent Maurice that he had purposely tried to wound her, sending his daughter to her with those ghastly flowers. "You are a most ungrateful man!" she thundered at him. "Haven't I treated you and your wife like brother and sister? Haven't I loved your children as though they were mine, as part of my family? And this is what you do in return!"

It was common knowledge among her friends that at times a very insignificant matter would send Helena into an apex of rage, while she would at other times pass up a grave situation with a smile. It all depended on the intensity of her phobias, grown out of her own tragic past—a sense of superstition that would magnify things out of proportion. Maurice, this time, was being his reasonable best, and tried in a gentle way to make her realize his innocence. That only made Helena turn on his wife. Georgie had done it, then. Georgie had sent her daughter to hurt her.

All explanations and protestations, all reasoning failed. Modjeska left the theatre in a dark mood, speaking to no one. It was a very sad afternoon for everyone. But especially for little Ethel who could understand nothing of the whole business, nor why her friend should cut her cold.

The affair was allowed to drop into the realm of forgotten things, and the friendship between Helena and Maurice continued. They went on to act in many plays together, for there was none who could play Armand or Orlando as Maurice could. And their successes were helped by the Company they had with them, by such excellent actors as William Owen; Ian Robertson, brother of Ferbes, stage manager and remarkable actor in his own right; the dainty Hamilton Bell; Mrs. Grace Henderson; Carhart, and others. Among the younger members of outstanding caliber was Robert Tabor, who worked out his parts with singular intelligence, and was soon to make his success as Macduff in London before his sudden death ended a career of unusual promise.

Finally, some discord arose between Helena and Maurice that time could not mend. Helena gave the story of the affair to her friend, the actress Ada Rehan:

I added *A Doll's House* to my repertoire, and I believe this was the first production of Henrik Ibsen's play on the English-speaking stage. But I am grieved to say that American audiences did not take to it. We had to drop it. However, the play inspired Maurice Barrymore to write the play he called *Nadjezda,* which did not have the slightest resemblance to Ibsen's play, with the exception of a desperate dance he introduced, the purpose of which was to keep the men from leaving the room. And this was not a tarantella, but a waltz.

We produced the play, but it proved so exhausting that after the first three weeks' run I had to take a rest. In Boston *Nadjezda* was played to packed houses, but Mr. Barrymore took it off the bill because I would not play it every night. He insisted that the play would make a great hit in London. He produced it there later, but it failed.

In this case, Helena did her best to keep a mere difference of opinion from breaking up their friendship. An abundance of gossip had for some time been spread abroad concerning their relationship, and this made it doubly hard for them to maintain a natural affection for each other.

"Later," explained Helena, "I introduced *Measure for Measure* to the American public. It had not been produced since Adelaide Neilson's time. During the same season, I presented *Daniela, Dona Diana,* and *Les Chouans.* Mr. Barrymore made a hit in the last play. It was based on Honoré de Balzac's novel of the same title and was written by Pièrre Berton, a very talented French actor and author. However, the play required such an elaborate production and so many actors that we could not keep it on the bills. The bulk of scenery and the number of extra men and women made the play hard to handle and carry about the country. Besides, we had our Shakespearean production, requiring not only scenery, but furniture and a great number of costumes. Nevertheless, Maurice insisted we must continue with *Les Chouans,* and here again we were up against a difference in opinion. But it was I who was responsible for the actor's salaries. And I could not afford to continue with the presentation of it. Even this did not break up our friendship. We had too much respect for each other. We were both creative artists and admired each other as such. We had much to contribute to each other. But he was stubborn! How stubborn he was! And I think I was worse. It was a common trait then, and subconsciously, I think, it pulled us together."

Here were two highly complex members of the theatre world, cutting out a lasting name for themselves in stage history, creating a source of legends even during their lifetime. They tried their best to work together and succeeded for some time. But inevitably they must part, even in friendship.

In later years they would meet again—chance re-encounters in New York, on the West Coast, or in Europe. These would be scenes of great emotional tenderness. Georgie would suffer pangs of jealousy. Helena would inquire after the children, speak again of the brilliant theatrical career that must be theirs, particularly Ethel's. She would never forget Ethel. It happened once that Helena, in an excess of love for the child, suggested she be allowed to pay for Ethel's education. The mother was deeply insulted. They were not in need of any charity. She condemned the suggestion as a blatant act of bad taste on Modjeska's part.

But Georgie Drew Barrymore knew nothing of the inner motivations of the Polish actress. She knew nothing of the deep moments of despair, the sense of deprivation, the emptiness. . . .

24. THE NEW ROLE

THE CHLAPOWSKI family became American citizens. Helena, however, always carried within her
a deep devotion for the country of her birth. At times she was
affected by an intense longing to return. Yet America had become her home. She had grown to love America, and America,
in turn, had come to think of her with pride as an American
rather than as a foreigner. Her husband, who had gradually
adjusted himself to a life on the fringes of a great career, followed suit, dropping his title. Rudolph changed his name to
Ralph. He had finished his schooling in Europe and the United
States. A brilliant student, he became a builder of bridges, and
was eventually elected Chairman of the board of engineers for
the San Francisco-Oakland bridge. This was the high point of
his life's work.

When in Poland, Helena had given up much of her time to
helping her country. Now in America she wanted to find ways
of helping Americans. That to her meant loving one's country.
She encouraged young students of acting to come to her with
their problems. She liked the company of the young and the
enthusiastic. She knew the great personages of the time, the
Shermans, the Grants, the Longfellows, the Whitmans, but she
chose to concentrate on the unknown actors, poets, painters, and
scientists. She gave financial aid whenever that was possible.
She searched for new talent to bring it into contact with the
famous and the influential. The new artists must be given a
chance to be heard. She dedicated much of her time to this work.
It was what made her life seem most worth while.

Helena toured the country with Otis Skinner as her leading
man. She became very attached to him, and unexpectedly was
able to do him a very good turn. It happened when she discovered a hidden acting talent in a young girl by the name of
Maude Durbin, an ambitious member of an old Missouri family. She coached the girl with great attention, taught her how to

198

play Shakespearean roles, received her into her touring Company. Maude's gifts were soon recognized, and she was hailed as a new American discovery. Otis Skinner fell in love with the girl and married her. Their child Cornelia Otis Skinner was to achieve fame as an actress and writer.

Modjeska became wealthy enough to buy a ranch, *Arden*, not far from Santa Ana in California. During her vacations she would invite the people with influence in artistic circles, together with the talented unknowns. In this way the young people would be given the right contacts. As for the students of acting, Helena would take them under her own guardianship. In the undistracted atmosphere of her beautiful home, discarding all formalities, and smoking her inevitable cigarettes, Helena would direct these young enthusiasts in the roles of Shakespeare, Goethe, Schiller, Molière, and other classics, and later in the roles of Ibsen.

Helena was always willing to give benefits when invited to do so. In 1888, in honor of Lester Wallack, much beloved actor-manager retiring from the stage, she played Ophelia to Edwin Booth's Hamlet at the Metropolitan Opera House in New York. Lawrence Barrett played the Ghost, Joseph Jefferson and W. J. Florence the Grave-diggers.

To help the oppressed Poles, Helena played with amateurs. In 1892 she was guest at the theatre of the Polish community in Chicago, known as Stanislawowo. She acted in two plays there, *Jadwiga: the Queen of the Lechites,* written by the stage manager, Szczesny Zahajkiewicz, and *Chlopi Arystokraci* by a writer in Poland, Wladyslaw Anczyc. The audience, made up of Polish exiles who had escaped the terror and misery of their own country, watching the scenes of rural life back home played so vividly by this great actress, were reduced to weeping without shame.

In 1893, at the Chicago World's Fair, Helena was invited by the Women's Congress to be guest speaker together with three other actresses—Clara Morris, Julia Marlowe, and Georgia Cayvan. For this occasion Modjeska dressed herself in a gown of red and white, the Polish national colors, and wore a diadem studded with diamonds. She looked like a queen and created a tremendous impression. She had recognized the chance

to make an anti-Russian speech before the world, for attending
the proceedings were both the American and European press.
She climaxed her speech by drinking a toast to America and the
freedom of Poland and dashing her glass against the wall,
while she cried out prophetically, "Like this glass now scattered
into pieces, let the empire of the Russian tyrants be broken."

When the news of this incident reached St. Petersburg, it
ended all chance of her returning to play in Warsaw or any
other part of Poland under Czarist rule. She had thought of
visiting the Russian theatres with a Shakespearean Company.
Now that plan was discarded.

That same day, when she returned to her private railroad car
at the Chicago station, the car she used throughout all her tours,
she found a man waiting to receive her. It was the handsome,
young, and impetuous Harrison Grey Fiske, editor of the New
York *Dramatic Mirror*. Helena had known him for some
years.

"Your maid let me see this remarkable car," he was saying as
he took her hand. "Marvelous! A palace on wheels! Pictures,
books, silver, all the conveniences. . . . But you deserve it. You
certainly do."

Helena smiled and asked the maid to bring a flask of wine
and some tea. Then she turned to him. "It's nice to see you here,
Grey. But you're traveling without Minnie? Aren't you lonely?
If I remember correctly you two were married some three years
ago. Minnie is a very sweet woman and a very good actress.
You should adore her."

Grey looked at his old friend and did not reply.

Helena noted the silence and chatted on. "Have you come to
talk business with me? Have you written a new play?"

As she threw her questions at him, her thoughts went back
to that New Year's Eve party she had given at her New York
apartment. Grey had been there. There was a lot of drinking
and Grey had taken too much. As she recalled the scene, she was
looking for her old maid Nastka. The four servants she had
hired for the occasion did not know where anything was, and
Nastka had wandered off somewhere. Grey was following her
around, insisting that he had fallen in love with her. She paid
little attention to him, until she went into the bedroom to see if

the maid was there. Then, still declaring his love, Grey had maneuvered her into a corner. Intoxicated both with alcohol and with admiration for the actress, he began to cover her with kisses. She managed to struggle out of his embrace and to get to the hall. He caught up with her and made excuses. Helena did not hold it against him. She smiled, as if to tell him they should forget about the whole thing. And they returned to the living room arm in arm, with none of the guests any the wiser. From then on, Grey had behaved like a gentleman toward her, but he looked for pretexts to be with her, to gaze into her large dark eyes and nothing more. He visited her many times to talk over some business proposition, to offer her a part in his play, or to get an interview for his paper.

Now, in the railroad car, he had something to tell her. He had become quite an influence in the theatre. He had a prosperous business in a rapidly developing field of show business. He was a writer, producer, and director. He rented theatres all over the country. Anything he had to say was important. He tried to sound important, businesslike, but he kept gazing into her eyes and losing himself in that old dream of loving her. "Yes. I have written another play. It's title is *Hester Creve*. I would like you to act in it, or at least to put in a good word for it." He hesitated. Was he sounding too eager? She seemed about to speak and he added hastily, "If you would only want to read it. . . ."

"Fine," Helena said, putting her hand on his. "Let me have it."

Encouraged by this gesture, he took a puff at his cigarette and continued talking. "I intend . . . or rather, I have already organized a company of players, the Manhattan Company. The aim is to produce the classics along with works of the most modern playwrights. You will be the star. I'll give you fifty per cent of all income. I have money. Next season we will rent the Manhattan Theatre in New York, and after success there we will tour the country. What do you think of that?"

It was a moment before she answered. "Lately, Grey, I don't think too much. I just grow older. But if you say you have money, why not spend it on your wife. Minnie is a good actress, I know. And she has the same color hair as mine, maybe even redder, which you like." She smiled at him. "Give Minnie a chance to swim out into the high seas of the American stage. You love her, don't you?"

Grey bowed his head, putting out his cigarette. He felt ashamed to be told of his responsibilities to his wife. But at the same time the thought troubled him that his wife occasionally met her first husband Le Grand White whom she had divorced. Grey couldn't help talking of it to Helena now. White was a musician and a producer. He had taught Minnie music, and set her on the stage, even with some success. She was still very fond of White. What was he to do?

But Helena was emphatic. "Stop behaving like a jealous child. I also have a second husband. What are a few husbands? As for women, they are like that—they remember a lot. Often they cannot quickly forget their first experiences. I'm sure there is nothing serious in it. Talk it over with her, why don't you? If she divorced him and married you, it means you are the one she chose to love. Think it over, and get rid of this jealousy. What a pity it is to waste this short life on petty things."

Grey thought over this advice. It was possible that Helena was right.

Helena offered him another cigarette from a small silver cigarette case, and she took one herself. But she said nothing more. She seemed to be waiting for his reaction. He looked up at her. "I agree. I think what you've said is good. I must do something about it." They had a drink, and his head felt clearer.

As he was leaving, Helena said, "Leave your play here. If I like it, I'll act in it, and if not I'll tell you so honestly. Perhaps some day I'll accept your offer to play in your Manhattan Company. You know Shakespeare is my favorite."

The next day, Harrison Grey Fiske returned to New York with the determination to make his wife a successful actress.

Minnie's first appearance was in Ibsen's *A Doll's House,* and she was a success. Her second play was her husband's *Hester Creve,* which failed. But Grey would not let her be discouraged. She went on, playing in Alphonse Daudet's *A White Pink,* Dumas' *La Femme de Claude,* Sardou's *Divorçons,* and even appeared in her own play, *A Light from St. Agnes.* She toured through the West and South. She showed herself to be an outstanding artist both in comedy and tragedy. In March, 1897, she played at the Fifth Avenue Theatre in New York in Lorimer Stoddard's dramatization of Thomas Hardy's *Tess of the D'Urbervilles*.

Finding himself with a famous actress for a wife, Grey fell in love with her all over again. Together they scored success after success and held a permanent position in the American theatre. They also had a private Pullman car in which they toured the country, playing in small towns and large, going into Canada and Mexico. Then, on returning home, they would retire to their little cottage at Larchmont where they rested, making long excursions in their little yellow cart.

There is no knowing what might have happened to the marriage of Grey and Minnie if it had not been for the friendly advice of Helena Modjeska. Minnie Maddern Fiske, in later years, thinking of the devotion of her husband toward the advancement of her career, praised the care with which he undertook the productions of the Manhattan Company. He was thorough about everything he did. It was he who made of her a real actress, she said. But when Grey looked back over his life's work, he always remembered that day in Chicago with gratitude. He never ceased to value the friendship of Modjeska, and though their paths diverged, he never forgot her kindness to him.

Helena was not lacking in those who recognized her contribution to the theatre in all its aspects. A man so restrained in his praise as Charles E. L. Wingate once said of Modjeska:

The chief glories of her record are her careful, enterprising attempts to hold on the stage the best and the rarest works of Shakespeare. All parts that Modjeska has essayed have been given with a womanly earnestness, an artistic sincerity, and an esthetic beauty that have made them warm, breathing characters of genuine interest and ennobling effect. Could the endowed theatre, which she has so long championed, be established, its influence upon the future of the American stage would become great—if at its head was an artist of the character and skill of Madame Modjeska.

25. THE LOST WOMAN

IN EXPERIENCE, character, and temperament, there was little in common between Helena Modjeska and Ada Rehan, an actress considerably younger than Helena. Nevertheless, the two women were thrown together in a most unusual way. The story was told by Helena herself, and found among her Polish papers.

Ada Rehan started her acting career at a very young age. Her older sister, Kate, had married Oliver Doud Byron, author and actor. It was through the Byrons that she got her start in the theatre. She was an attractive girl. A pair of light-gray Irish eyes sparkled in a delicately pale face. She had a slightly upturned nose, and her brown hair came down over her forehead in carefully tended bangs. She was a truly Celtic type, with a highly mobile face, which served her well in the many parts she played, from comedy to romantic tragedy. Despite her rather pert expression, she was tall in stature, and moved about the stage, as she did in life, with considerable grace, and indeed with an economical calculation as though nothing was done without the deepest premeditation. The truth was Ada Rehan was afraid of life beyond the theatre, and although she had two brothers and two sisters, all in the theatre, she was quite lonely. In compensation, she surrounded herself with dogs and other animal pets, for which she seemed to show greater preference than for humans.

It was while she was playing in her brother-in-law's play, *Across the Continent* in Newark, New Jersey, that she received the admiring attention of Augustin Daly. For many years Daly had been drama critic of the *New York Courier,* but was already launching out on his great career as playwright and producer. He approached Ada with the idea that she join the Company that he was then in the act of organizing. She was attracted by his air of politeness, but something in his laughing green eyes made her hesitate. He praised her acting in the most flattering

204

terms, and she was pleased. But she was also suspicious. Was he really after her talent? Or was it herself he wanted? She rather suspected the latter.

The more she reasoned it out, the more certain she became, and the more angered. The Byrons did not want to let Ada leave, and she felt most indebted to them, but to spite Mr. Augustin Daly she had to make a move that would make him see how she felt. She joined the Company of Mrs. John Drew at the Arch Street Theatre in Philadelphia.

From this Company she graduated to the stock Company of Macauley's Theatre in Louisville. In this way six years passed, in which Ada gained a certain position for herself in the theatre. Augustin Daly did not lose track of her. Every chance he got he urged her to join his Company. She evaded him just as studiously. It was a cat-and-mouse game between the two of them, but she did not need him now. Edwin Booth engaged her for his troupe, and she played Ophelia opposite his Hamlet. She played with John McCullough as Lady Anne in *Richard III*. Later it was opposite Lawrence Barrett, John T. Raymond, John Brougham, and with Adelaide Neilson. She rose to the position of a star among stars, and while she became famous and wealthy, she became more and more secluded in her private life, living in a New York mansion that cost her thirty thousand dollars, among her monkeys and dogs and cats.

Just about the time when Augustin Daly had given up all hope of winning Ada over, she, as is the case with most secretive women of her type, came to him by herself. It was general knowledge among the actors of his Company that Mr. Daly had strong feelings about Ada Rehan. He, of course, was overjoyed at the sight of her, but he maintained a cool front and signed her up as the star of his Company.

At this time, Daly was in his early forties, a man of genius, with a powerful personality. Mary Young, a member of his Company, who described him as having "extraordinary eyes of green, as clear and sharp as they were kind and laughing, wonderful, all-seeing eyes," wrote down an account of his strict and efficient manner of running his theatre. "Every member, with the exception of Miss Rehan, seemed to be in a state of complete terror. Rules and regulations were posted everywhere.

One: 'The way to succeed—mind your own business'; Two: 'How to be happy—keep your mouth shut.' I was amazed to see some extra girls hide behind pieces of scenery rather than face those remarkable eyes that might be cast their way as Mr. Daly was casually passing from one part of the stage to another."

To show off the universality of the woman he loved, Daly began reviving such old English comedies as *The Country Wife, She Would and She Would Not,* and *The Inconstant.* He made translations and adaptations of German and French authors. He toured with Ada across America and Europe. For several years he concentrated upon Shakespearean plays with Ada always playing the lead. In fact, in a few short years he had built up her reputation as a remarkable actress in tragedy and comedy alike, the talk of New York, Paris, London, Hamburg, and Berlin.

But Augustin Daly was a man of ever higher plans, of new ventures. He had no desire to fall into a rut. He had raised Ada to the top rung of fame. There was little more he could do for her. There were other actresses, perhaps even greater. He owed it to himself to look around. The fact was, he told himself, he was getting tired of cats and dogs and monkeys and their odd mistress. He began to correspond with Helena Modjeska. Perhaps he could get her to join his Company. Being a thorough man, he went to see her, and was certainly drawn to her. Then accidentally Ada discovered what was going on.

By this time, Ada had no need to worry about lack of engagements. There were plenty of producers in the United States who would snap her up at the chance; there was Herr Possat with his standing invitation to play with him in Munich, and Sarah Bernhardt wanted her to appear in Paris. Why should she cling to Augustin? She had a profound distrust of all men. And yet the letters addressed to Modjeska, and the knowledge that he was actually seeing Modjeska, stirred up new emotions in her secret heart. She was forced to admit to herself that she was jealous. The years of being with Augustin had done their work. She had become more attached to him than to her cats and dogs and monkeys. Without Augustin, she told herself, she would never be able to go on living, let alone acting.

She had heard much of Helena Modjeska, most of it gossip and hearsay. She had even seen her and met her and watched her. The resulting concept of Helena filled her with the desire to take swift and desperate action. And still she hesitated. She hated publicity of any kind, and her dislike of snooping reporters amounted to something of a phobia. She could tolerate adverse comments on her acting, even when playing the roles that she believed Shakespeare had destined for herself alone. But the possibility of any personal criticism bearing on her private world sent a cold fear into her blood. Above all, then, she must act in secrecy.

At this time Modjeska was in Paris. The first step in Ada's plan was to have it noised abroad that she had decided to settle down in Paris, and that she was inviting her friends to a house-warming. She sent no invitation to Modjeska by mail, but went personally to the Modjeska establishment to urge her to be sure to come. She contrived to make Helena feel that she thought the Polish actress the greatest of her time in any country, and that she was inviting to her party the cream of the theatre world. Helena simply must come, and so forth.

On arrival, Helena was puzzled to find no one present except her hostess, who seemed in a tense and excitable state. The place seemed prepared for the absent guests, the tables covered with food and drink, the lights dimmed to give a sense of mystery to the room, somber with its gilded furniture and gilded picture frames in true French splendor, while cats padded like shadows across a silken carpet.

Ada was all attention as she begged Helena to make herself comfortable. She had so longed, she said, for this chance to have a quiet and deliciously intimate chat with so great an artist as Madame Modjeska. When Helena asked about the party, Ada confessed quite blandly that there would be no party. This was all a ruse to get Helena over to her house alone.

"But did you have to go to all this trouble just for that? Why couldn't you talk to me at my house?"

Ada smiled somewhat slyly, and without an answer she picked up a gold-rimmed decanter and began mixing some sort of drink of a pinkish hue. Helena was too curious to feel exasperated. She watched Ada, fascinated, and began to imagine

what it must be like to find oneself a potential poison victim.
There was such an air of determination about Ada at that moment, and Helena had heard of Ada's reputation for mixing
rare potions that mysteriously put her guests in a favorable and
receptive frame of mind. She had already thought of that. She
fell back on a trick she had used many times before to fortify
herself against the effects of strong liquor, that of eating fat
ham or plain salt pork with black rye bread before arriving at a
party, and as a consequence she would remain sober long after
other guests had become completely befuddled. Helena could
see the glint in Ada's eyes and surmised that something special
was in store for her. Nevertheless, she decided, no matter what
the consequences, to submit to the experiment to the bitter end.

They drank. First to mutual success; second to health; and
at the third their heads went into a dizzy spin.

There was a long silence. Ada put a hand on Helena's wrist
and held it there. She seemed to want to speak of things of great
import, but her tongue failed her, and she was too embarrassed
to take her hand away. The autumn rain was pecking at the
windows. At last Ada raised her head and stared at Helena out
of dazed gray eyes. She said slowly, "Augustin is leaving me."

"For whom?"

Ada withdrew her hand and placed it carefully in her lap beside her other one. Helena's thoughts went back to a conversation she had had with Augustin Daly a few days back. He was
offering her an exclusive contract and a tour over Europe with
a Shakespearean repertoire. So that was it!

Before she could speak, Ada's large eyes came up again, and
the slow voice was saying, "He wants to leave me and go after
you."

"Impossible!" Helena cried out. "Of course, it's true that he
offered me parts in a few plays, which, to tell you the truth, he
felt were more suitable to my talents than yours. But that's as
far as it went. Ada, that's surely no reason for believing he
wants to leave you for me."

"No? And how about the tender letter he wrote to you the
other day?"

"What letter?"

"Oh, I intercepted that one."

Helena stared. "But Ada, that can't be. Augustin knows that I am married. Besides, I have my own theatrical Company. Why should I want to join another one, even if it is Daly's?"

Ada's face was full of distrust as she looked from the face of her guest to the crystal decanter. She reached out a hand and filled up their glasses again.

"Let's have a drink."

Helena barely suppressed a smile. "What are you trying to do? Get me drunk in the hope that you can squeeze some secret out of me?"

Ada evaded her eyes.

"Or perhaps you want to poison me."

"Poison!" Ada looked at her, seriously shocked. "But I'm drinking the same as you, how can you be afraid of poison?"

They drank the fourth glass.

Ada's eyes came up to Helena's again. Such soft gray eyes. "You wouldn't want my spirit to torture you, would you? . . . Like Igo's."

Helena jumped up. Her blood rushed to her head. "How did you find out about Igo?"

"I know everything about you," cried Ada, as she struggled to her feet. "You have a fatal hold over men. You will ruin Augustin as you've ruined others, as well as ruining me." Ada was beside herself, as she rushed over to Helena and began embracing her wildly. "I implore you to leave him alone. Please, please, please. . . ."

Helena tried to quiet her. "Ada, you shouldn't let your imagination run away with you. It's because you live alone with nothing but these animals for company. As for me, I have a clear conscience and I tell you this on my honor—I have no desire to take him away from you. I know that you love him, Ada."

They sat down on the sofa, holding hands, each looking into the other's eyes. All at once Ada jumped up. "I will show you the letter he wrote to you. It's probably one of many such love notes."

She reached under the cushion, a design of flowers and canine heads.

Helena insisted, "I have never received any love letters from Mr. Daly."

"Read," said Ada with a flourish, holding out the letter.

"Perhaps he wrote one then, but he never sent a letter to me outside of the business letter about the tour."

"Read," said Ada again.

Helena took the letter and started to read, but her head began to spin. The letters on the page played strange tricks, at one time growing immense like mountains, then shrinking up to tiny reptiles, finally fading out altogether. "You got me drunk," she muttered. "Did you want to murder me?"

"If it's poison, I shall die too."

"What satisfaction could I get out of that?" asked Helena.

"Don't be silly." Ada promptly filled the glasses.

Helena read on, trying to concentrate on the context as best she could. It was in fact a love letter, not at all like the correct and ever-sober Augustin Daly. She could not reach the end of the letter. A thick fog had entered her brain. She dropped and her head sagged into Ada's lap, as she kept trying to talk.

"You should try to understand . . . be sensible, Ada. I am old already, and have other loves I am pledged to . . . Igo . . . the theatre . . . why should I need Daly? You shouldn't be so naïve, Ada. He doesn't mean a thing to me . . . not as a man to go to bed with. . . . You're young . . . you love him. . . . Why should I . . . ?"

Her words faded out. She had lost consciousness. Ada sat quite still with Helena's head on her knees. Her eyes stared with a dull stupor at the opposite wall, ornate with portraits of cats and dogs. Slowly her eyes dropped and her head came down on her chest.

Minutes and hours made their flight, and the two women held their positions without a move. The rain outside was lashing down in torrents, smashing against the window panes like maddened drummers. Two pekinese dogs came in from another room and forlornly cruised around the table, looking up at their mistress with their bulging sad eyes. The sound of the storm disturbed them. In vain they looked up for some sign of affection from their mistress, and shivered at her feet.

It was past midnight when Augustin Daly walked into the apartment. Seeing the two actresses on the sofa and the half-filled glasses on the table, he surmised what had happened. He

got ice water to bathe their faces. Helena was the first to recover. She opened her eyes with a groan. "She wanted to poison
me."

Daly smiled as he turned to work on Ada.

The evening ended with a long conversation among the three
of them. Augustin succeeded in convincing Ada of his love for
her, and of Helena's innocence.

Ada Rehan continued to appear under Daly's direction, and
he enlarged her repertoire by three roles, Roxane in *Cyrano de
Bergerac,* Portia in *The Merchant of Venice,* and Lady Garnet
in *The Great Ruby.*

In June of 1899, Augustin Daly died in Paris. Ada was at his
side. Less than two years later, Ada withdrew from the stage
completely and lived alone among her dogs and cats in a cottage
on the Cumberland shore of the Irish Sea.

26. AN UNEXPECTED VISIT

After making her name in the United States as the
greatest Shakespearean actress, it had been no difficult task for Modjeska to conquer Britain. But there was no
more fertile ground than the United States, a youthful country,
expanding its industries, its farms, growing fabulous in wealth,
looking to the theatre for its culture. One could tour the country again and again and always be sure of enthusiastic welcome.

Modjeska was famous and rich and loved. She had everything an actress could well desire. But she did not forget those
who had need of help. She was spending the summer of 1902
at her California home when she received a letter from Jozef
Kotarbinski, the director of the Cracow Theatre. He was desperate. The theatre was losing money. Without a second
thought, Helena decided to hasten to Poland for a tour without
remuneration, and was even prepared to put up money of her
own.

On her way over, she stopped on the shores of the Lakes of
Killarney. Some years before, she had stayed there a few days
and met John Singer Sargent. The romantic style of his painting and the courtliness of his manner reminded her so much of
Igo. There, too, she had met George Bernard Shaw for the
first time. Years had passed, but the lakes were unchanged in
their severe Irish beauty. It was only the people who aged, forgetting their past. Yet, Helena was an exception in this. She
remained young in spirit, in her appearance, in everything but
the marks left upon her noble features by her frequent attacks
of melancholy.

She stopped at Paris, but she felt that things had changed
there. The atmosphere, a great romantic tradition, had vanished. She stood in front of Victor Hugo's house, and felt this
change more deeply than at any other time. It was now owned
by some wealthy businessman. She thought of Hugo's fiery de-
fiance of Napoleon III. She recalled his words in 1871 on his

212

return to his beloved city from exile in the Channel Islands. The character of this great writer fascinated Helena, particularly his modest way of living, while distributing his earnings among the poor. She could never forget a particular incident she had witnessed in the street. An old, old woman was walking by the railings of the Luxembourg, bowed down by the weight of the laundry she was carrying. Quite suddenly, Monsieur Hugo appeared, thrust some coins into her hand, and talked to her. He then proceeded down the street, carrying her load for her, while she trotted alongside, gleefully counting the money in her hand. Helena had followed them, and a little while later came upon him face to face. She remembered what he had told her then, speaking of her acting:

"Music gives expression to that which cannot be said in words, but on which it is impossible to be silent. Your acting on the stage, Madame, is precisely that kind of music."

He asked her then to appear in his play *Ruy Blas* at the Théâtre Odéon. But that had been many years ago. Victor Hugo passed into eternity in 1885. The streets without him were empty. Paris had no more of his kind.

Helena arrived in Cracow in September, 1902. After Cracow she would visit Lwow and Poznan. There could be no question of her visiting Warsaw. The Czarist administration was threatening to arrest her on sight. At this time the whole of Russia and the occupied lands of Poland were in turmoil. The oppressed peoples of Russia were demanding freedom from tyranny within their own borders. The Czarist regime doubled its watchdogs, determined to keep out foreign influence toward dangerous liberalism.

Despite her desire to get to work quickly, Helena was forced to delay her first stage appearance for several months. The rigors of travel, the adjustment to change of climate, together with the emotional effect of seeing so many old friends and places, combined to put her in a state of nervous exhaustion. On her doctor's advice, she left Cracow for Cirkvenica in Dalmatia to recuperate.

In the meantime the Polish papers were working the people up to a state of eager anticipation with their retelling of her successes in *Macbeth, Much Ado About Nothing, Mary Stuart,* in the plays of Ibsen and Sudermann, and by their talk of a play by Stanislaw Wyspianski, entitled *Warszawianka,* in which she was to appear as Maria. Some time before, this Polish author had sent a published copy of his play to Helena in America with an admiring dedication. In her turn, Helena was able to say of it:

"My part in *Warszawianka* inspired me from the first reading. The spirit of nationalism was never foreign to me, and I liked the down-to-earth quality of the play. Whereas the transformation of the orphaned sweetheart into a Polish Cassandra was so deftly handled by the author that it immediately caught hold of me so that memorizing Maria's lines was a simple task."

The heroine of this play was hardly twenty-five, and the actress to play her was then more than twice as old. But so long as Modjeska played the role, it never seemed to matter. It is probable that an actress of less experience than Modjeska would never have been able to inject the power of personality needed at the end of the play when Maria learns that the battle has been lost. The young actor Ludwik Solski, who played the role of Wiarus, described how at that moment Modjeska's acting began mounting to a steady climax, to the high point of intensity where she cried out to the embattled soldiers, "Fly on, our eagle, fly, fly!"

The author himself, standing behind the scenes in a high-buttoned black coat, was so moved by the performance that he began to tremble like a child, and when the young Solski passed him on the way to his dressing room to remove his make-up, Wyspianski threw his arms around him, clinging for support, and he would not let go until Helena's last speech had died away into silence.

The curtain came down in the silence that reigned through the audience. Everyone was so crushed by the magnificence of Modjeska's acting that it was a few minutes before they recovered and burst into deafening applause. The curtain was raised again to reveal Modjeska standing before them, head bowed. She seemed the spirit of youth, "as beautiful as a rose," said Solski later. The audience got to its feet, cheering. Solski was still standing in the wings, too stunned with emotion to move, when he felt the author shaking his arm: "Lead me on to the stage." Dressed in his soldier's make-up, Solski stumbled onto the stage leading the trembling Wyspianski like a blind man. The poet stood before Helena, the cheers from the audience rising up to them like a wall of sound. From under his coat Wyspianski pulled a silver wreath with white ribbons and placed it on Helena's head.

The critics who had seen Modjeska play sixteen of Shakespeare's great roles were certain that Shakespeare was her forte, but the dramas of Stanislaw Wyspianski were of an entirely different type. The structure of scenes was different. They moved in an atmosphere of symbolism, now national, now universal, taxing the actor to the utmost in his attempt to reveal the intensity of their meaning.

While she was in Lwow, Helena was able to see for herself a production of *Wesele* by the same author. She talked to Tadeusz Pawlikowki who presented the play, and told him, "This author claws at my heart. He opens up new wounds, makes the old ones bleed again. My soul begins burning. I feel that the poet is reaching down to the depth of human degradation and stirring up tragic storms never felt before by anyone, and that to give expression to them he is finding a new language and a new form."

The emotional impact of Wyspianski's writing upon the actress impelled her to undertake the study of the most difficult role in the whole of the poet's work, the part of Laodamia from the tragedy *Protesilas i Laodamia,* and she decided to include the play in her repertoire.

When she left for a short rest at the Rzegocin estate below Poznan, she had with her Polish translations of Shakespeare, *La Gioconda* by Gabriele D'Annunzio, and *Protesilas i Laodamia.* She began her work on the last two with the energy and enthusiasm of youth, but her strength did not seem equal to it. Her doctors were concerned that her state of tension, aggravated by a kidney and heart ailment, would prove decisive. When the journalist Bartoszewicz of a Cracow daily dug up old gossip about the actress, it brought her face to face with those things in the past she wanted most to forget.

At last she wrote a letter to her friend Lucyna, the wife of director Kotarbinski: "I beg you to tell me sincerely whether you really count on my new appearance in Cracow and whether my participation will really help you with conditions as they are now? If your husband has already completed some preparation for the plays I am appearing in, I will of course fulfill my promise, but if not, frankly, I would rather not play."

But she did not know that the announcement of her reappearance in Cracow had stirred the whole of Poland. Hundreds of letters had already arrived from every part of the country asking for tickets. Groups from Russian-occupied Poland were preparing pilgrimages to Cracow to see the famous actress. From Warsaw, from Vienna, and even from Moscow and Praha, the devotees of theatre were preparing themselves for this trip to Cracow to see and hear at least once in their lifetime the illustrious Modjeska.

Lucyna and her husband sent letters and telegrams to Rzegocin imploring Helena to join them. Thereupon Helena disregarded the advice of all doctors and left for Cracow. She started rehearsals. The doctors hovered about her in agitation. Her physical condition did not permit her working so hard. Helena refused to listen to them when they talked of her withdrawing from the stage. Her life was the stage. How could she live without the stage? The doctors were reduced to posting a constant watch over her. There was always one of them in her dressing room ready for an emergency.

The stage decor for *Protesilas i Laodamia* was designed by the author, himself a painter of recognized ability. It was not long before the director, Kotarbinski, was storming about the theatre, tearing his hair. The cost of the production was mounting steadily. The idea of the production, he exclaimed, was to make money for the theatre, not to lose it. The theatre could not afford to put up so much money before the opening. But Wyspianski had his dream of how the play should be staged and he fought for the inclusion of every detail. It was Helena who brought peace between the two men by investing her own money in the show to cover the extra cost. For she agreed with the author that the play should be done exactly as he had imagined it. Wyspianski's genius should not be thwarted by details.

Helena sincerely admired Wyspianski. She did not allow her

own great stature as an artist or her own superb understanding of the actor's art to stand as a barrier between herself and the author. Wyspianski had the reputation of being a quiet and unassuming man, but she encouraged him to talk to her, to express his ideas on the playing of her part. He slowly opened up to her, until he was able to transfer to her the full force of his inspiration. He even read Sophocles to her in the original, to get her into the mood and to awaken a deep sense of the Greek rhythm. His reading of Sophocles so appealed to Helena that she decided at once she must play *Antigone,* and portray the heroine's struggles against the tyranny of the King of Thebes.

Kotarbinski agreed to this plan and both plays were produced, one as seen by the eyes of Sophocles and the other by a contemporary playwright. Helena played both roles with such an incredible depth of expression and insight that they were never forgotten, and it was felt by all present that Modjeska had reached a power in the final suicide scene of Wyspianski's drama that was truly sublime.

Among those who came to thank her was Gabryela Zapolska. It had been a matter of three decades since Helena had first met Gabryela. Gabryela had then been an ambitious young actress of a wild, ungovernable nature that made her, in many respects, so much like Helena had been at the start of her career. Before Helena had met her, someone in the girl's theatrical Company had reported to the Russian authorities in Warsaw certain stories concerning Gabryela's activities, both political and moral. As a result the girl was ostracized by upper-class society and refused permission to enter any theatre dressing room. When Helena heard about the fate of the girl, and of her ambitions as an actress and writer, she promptly went to see her, invited her to share her dressing room, and promised her all possible assistance.

Gabryela had never forgotten this noble impulse on Helena's part. The thirty years before Helena's return to Poland had not seen Gabryela's rise to any glory as an actress, but she had become Poland's most outstanding woman playwright, and hearing of Helena's decision to return for a tour of Poland, she wrote especially for Modjeska a one-act play *Jesienny Wieczor.* It was to be the last play Helena would do in the old country.

The phenomenal acclaim received by Modjeska on her return to the Polish stage made her the talk of the town. It seemed that everyone was discussing her career and her life, and what was not known about her was vastly conjectured. It was a situation ripe for gossip, and her enemies, motivated by jealousy or political animosity, made the most of it. The busy little journalist Bartoszewicz whipped up his campaign against her, both in the press and the cafés.

Helena was unable to ignore the gossip and slander, and at one time she was heard to exclaim, "The greatest injustice was meted out to me by my own home town, by my own people! I shall never forget that!"

The vicious tongues were doing their work of poisoning her mind. She was becoming obsessed by a sense of horrible guilt due to the growing conviction that she had been responsible for the deaths of Igo, Gustav, and even of her daughter Marylka. Day and night to Helena became fused into one long nightmare of torture. She began to behave as if under the influence of some drug. She spent her days on her bed smoking incessantly. She would lie there, lost in her troubled thoughts, long into the night. Then she would suddenly spring to life, run out of the house, and walk the empty streets for hours at a time.

Sometimes she would walk to the Botanical Gardens. She would even go to the bench on Chestnut Alley, where Igo had been sitting when she returned to Cracow that early summer morning long ago. She remembered well how he had looked, how the pigeons had circled over his head, how they covered him from head to foot as he held out bread crumbs, and how she had startled him by her sudden appearance.

But now there was only night, night, night. Cracow slept in the humid heat. Cracow, the city of those who labored all day, slumbered in sweat. And the black night hung over Cracow like a monk's cowl. The ugliness of the city was nicely concealed by the night.

Helena soon became absorbed in the concept of an oblivious night, one which did not examine or question, one which smothered even the most infinitesimal light. It appeared that both the Botanical Gardens and the world were enveloped in this tragic night, from which there was no disentanglement. This evil, stifling night spelled doom to golden thoughts. There could be no talk of suffering in such an impact of darkness. For suffering, like marriage, remained a great educator. One spoke of neither, because marriage was the beginning of birth, and suffering was the beginning of death. But one had to have courage.

Helena sprang up from the park bench, and began walking briskly without looking back. She began to feel as light as a bird in flight. A gentle breeze blew in from somewhere, played around the folds of her long lace gown, blew up to her face and tossed her hair. She felt the coolness of it upon her skin, and a shiver passed from her head to her burning feet.

Before long she found herself on the open meadow of St. Sebastian, and from there, breathing hard, but without slackening her pace, she sped on to the house of the Neufelds in Krzemionki.

Helena was not surprised to see the lights on in the corner room. She was convinced that they would be waiting for her there. She approached the window. Inside, a very old woman was moving about the room. There was a high candle in the center of the table, and the table was covered with pots. The old woman was peering into the pots, and now and again stirring with a long spoon. This was Igo's mother. Helena knew it at once. There was no surprise in her mind at finding her there, only surprise that Madame Neufeld failed to come over to her. She knocked on the window. The old lady trotted to the window and tried to see who her late visitor was. There was a smile of childish expectation on her face that made her look very little older than when Helena had last seen her. In a moment she appeared to recognize Helena. She moved quickly back and disappeared.

Presently, the door was opened, and Madame Neufeld was beckoning Helena in. "Please, do come in. I was expecting you. I am alone in the house. The fact is I have been alone many years. Igo moved out, and the doctor moved out soon after. You knew my husband? Oh, but you did! You used to visit Igo here. Do you remember the great fire? Ah, you were so beautiful and young! Igo loved you. Do you remember?"

They stood facing each other, the candlelight playing on their faces. The air was damp in the room, and their faces gleamed with perspiration. The strangest mixture of smells played about the room. Madame Neufeld went from window to window pulling down the shades, giving Helena time to look about the room. The furniture looked much as she remembered it thirty years before. The walls were covered with old photographs and pictures in black frames. But everything was blanketed by the curling clouds of steam rising up from the pots on the table, and it was from these pots that the mixture of smells arose.

"Come over to the table," said Madame Neufeld. "I'm calling Igo to come over tonight. He will surely come to honor you. He loved you."

Helena's whole body shook convulsively as she approached the table. The old woman was stirring the liquid in the pots again. Helena could see that the pots contained herbs and flowers. In some seemed to be yellow flowers, in others red, and in still others only green plants. Madame Neufeld was soon stirring the liquid in the pots with such skill and swiftness that the liquids were all swirling simultaneously. The steam began to shoot up to the ceiling, where it coiled and spread, and slid down the walls. The old woman made the air restless with her stirring arm, so that shoots of steam would play out at the sides, and hover like branches or shrubs. The whole room in Helena's mind took on the appearance and sensation of a tropical jungle, pervaded with an odor that was sickening and sweet at the same time.

"It's good, it's good!" Madame Neufeld was muttering. "He will come tonight. The Vistula will let him out. The river is kinder than humans. He was a good boy."

She suddenly bent and blew out the candle on the table, as she called out with a piercing voice as if her child were in a far field, "Igo! Igo! Come, Igo! Come here into the house."

Helena watched as if in a trance, her eyes staring at the steam as if she expected Igo to appear out of the curling mass. Indeed, the constant stirring of the spoons and the dizzying spin of liquids, as the old woman's hand moved faster and faster, seemed to cast a spell upon Helena, and she swayed back and forth to the sound of the old woman's chant.

"Igo come back! Igo come in! Igo be seen! . . ." The old woman's face had become a bloody red. Her voice was becoming a scratch. Yet she continued the ritual with an ever-increasing intensity, until she seemed to be begging desperately for something to happen. Then abruptly her voice broke off in the middle of her son's name, and she slipped to the floor, a hoarse cry coming out of her throat. Helena stood motionless beside the old woman's body, her lips moving silently.

Slowly the strange jungle of steam began to buckle and fold, as if shrinking, until it was stretching itself out along the floor. It was difficult to breathe in all that density of sickly sweetness. Helena raised her hand to her forehead, felt her hair—everything was wet. Her clothes clung to her as though she had walked into some warm lake. She moved back to the door and opened it to let in the air. It seemed to strike her in the face to bring back a sense of clarity. The old woman did not stir. Helena moved over to her, struck by a sudden fear, but found her breathing in short gasps as a dog breathes. She stooped over and began dragging the woman to a chair. She was suddenly conscious of how light her old body was. Helena pressed her lips to the woman's forehead in sudden, painful love.

Madame Neufeld had opened her eyes, and now spoke reassuringly, in short bursts of phrases. "But you must not worry. He will certainly come. We'll try again. I will have to get some more water. I must heat it more, still more. The Vistula is cold, so cold. . . ."

Helena slid to the floor at the old woman's feet and was silent. From outside, far off, the plaintive cry of dogs could be heard. It was the pleading of beasts that wished to be free to roam the fields but were held back by the chains of humans. Helena could hear the breathing of Madame Neufeld. It was heavy still, but even. She was returning slowly to normal life. With her bony hand she felt out Helena's fingers resting on the chair arm. She pressed them lightly.

Helena looked up. Madame Neufeld was nodding her head slowly. Something of the old dignity of Igo's mother had returned, and she spoke quietly.

"Igo will have to come because you are here in Cracow. His love for you was great, and if he did not come tonight, it was merely because some business of importance held him back. Tomorrow we must go and visit him. He will be pleased."

27. THREE LOVERS

THE VISTULA River slipped through the warm meadows. The darkness of evening came down saturated with young voices singing and laughing. This was to be a night of surprises. Bonfires and torches sprang into agitated dance on the banks, neutralizing the light of stars, until the sky shone like the armor of some medieval and giant knight. Wreaths of flowers were tossed on the waters. Screams and excited laughter marked the swift launching of boats from the shore. Each boy was in wild pursuit of the wreath of his girl, while the girls stood on the banks, lustily singing:

> "Our mothers knew and passed it on,
> They'd heard the same from theirs in turn,
> That on this night of St. John
> A sobotka always burned. . . ."

It was the beginning of an old song written by Jan Kochanowski, and nothing had changed the custom for hundreds of years. Perhaps the joy was greater, and the youths more numerous. But the faces of the young people radiated the same excitement of an unknown future.

Helena walked slowly along the bank, a ghost of forty years ago. She knew no one here now. The young girls and boys of her own youth stayed away. Some had died, some had left the country and lived in exile, others were too weighed down with the cares of living to give a thought to the St. John's night of their past. Helena felt an insurmountable sadness. She walked through the celebrating crowds, skirting the blazing bonfires. Nevertheless, her path was lonely. None of the youths paid any attention to her, or if some boy or girl looked up in time to notice her, passing sedately in her long white dress, it was to think fleetingly that here was an old witch, trying to ruin the night for the young ones.

The sand rustled under her feet, and her eyes looked over

223

the surface of the waters. Vaguely in her mind was the thought that she was looking for someone. Now and then she would turn her face to the left across the stretch of reeds and brush, and she would watch the flickering lights of the city. Sometimes she would accidentally step on an abandoned wreath. She would pick it up, shake out the sand, and throw it on the waters, murmuring to herself, "Float on, float on, far, far away. For no one should ever find you." Her face would light up with an ironic smile, and she seemed to hold within her a mystery that could not be solved.

As she walked on, it seemed as if the youthful laughter of the crowds followed her, rolling along the banks, and at her heels. Laughter, as everything in this world, had its beginning back there where St. John's night was in full fling, but it had its end right here where she walked, sinking into the wet sand beside her. For the boys and girls celebrating, this laughter could mean the birth of eternal love, but for Helena it meant only bitter memories.

At once Helena became possessed by a new thought. She remembered Sarah Jewett, a young American girl, an actress, who loved to walk the streets around Broadway at night. Sarah had large, elated, expectant black eyes. The strange unreal quality of the girl attracted Helena. To be with her and talk with her was to be carried into a dream world, a world of imagination. Her presence made Helena forget her own problems, her own miseries. She could go with Sarah into that world of fantasy, the land of eternal youth.

But Sarah did not live in the real world too long. She died mysteriously in a New York asylum, leaving nothing behind her, and with no relatives to claim her. In Sarah's empty apartment Helena came upon a strange poem written by the girl, which she had entitled *Why?* That was all that remained of Sarah Jewett. Helena carried this poem with her wherever she went, although she showed it to no one. She had read the poem over so many times that she had learned it by heart, and would say the lines to herself when she took her walks, whether in New York, San Francisco, London, or Paris:

"When love must bring regret,
I would forget—and yet
For memories' rapturous pain,
My heart would yearn again.
Ah me! Why would it be?

I know that love is blind,
That so it is more kind.
And yet in my delight,
I long for perfect light.
Ah me! It must not be!

I wonder if love meant
To yield no full content.
And yet, for some reply
That does not come, I sigh.
Ah me! It cannot be!"

Helena knew full well that artistically this was merely minor verse. Sarah had no great talent, even as an actress. Nevertheless, Helena could see that it did succeed in expressing something of the complexities of the girl's soul, and it was obvious that Sarah wanted to leave after her nothing but this one poem. Now walking along the path beside the Vistula, Helena thought of the lovely black eyes of Sarah Jewett. The girl had been ripe for love, and yet it had been an unfulfilled love affair that had driven her away from harsh reality and into some world of her own imagining.

Helena slowed her steps and stared about her. What had made her think of Sarah now? This was St. John's night, when love bloomed in the embraces of boys and girls. The reeds beside her stirred in the wind a while, and her thoughts sped back to that night when she escaped from the convent . . . and he. . . . Helena quickly walked on, passing groups that grew smaller. She was moving up the bank, where there were fewer wreaths, less noise, fewer lights. People were left behind. Helena did not feel tired as she walked on. Her shoes were heavy with sand, but she did not slacken her pace. She had entered a more beautiful world, where the grass was taller, and the reeds denser, and the stars brighter, for there were no bonfires here. It was a more tolerable world for Helena. The soft music of the waters came to her ears and soothed her. She was held by a strange peace. Was it as if she had drawn near to him?

Somehow it came as no surprise to Helena to find Igo's mother standing in front of her.

"So you knew about this place?" said the old woman with a sparkling, birdlike expression.

Almost without being aware of it, Helena took the woman's arm, and both stood silently with their eyes upon the Vistula.

There was a community of feeling between them and both sensed it. They were seeking him out, one her son, the other her lover. Presently Madame Neufeld began whispering some mysterious words, perhaps a prayer to the river and the light-footed wind that seemed to pluck the unintelligible sounds and waft them across the gleaming monster, the star-lit Vistula. She paused for an answer, but the waters swayed on as before.

She turned to Helena eagerly. "Let's make a fire. Igo will see the flames and will come to visit us."

"Yes," Helena agreed.

For several minutes they both worked in silence, gathering dried sticks and anything that would be likely to burn, piling them in one spot. Madame Neufeld came upon a discarded, dried-up wreath, and placed it on top of the heap.

"That's your old wreath," she said.

"Mine?"

"Of course. Who else would leave it here so that it could get so dry?"

Helena could not think of an answer to that. For both women the concept of time had vanished. Years and hours had no more reality. No more could they reason what they planned to do. Their love was eternal, unlimited by logic.

Helena found another dried-up wreath, and added it to the pile. The old woman stared at it in astonishment. "Oh" she murmured, and began gathering fuel with still greater speed. She searched for dried-up flowers and with the rising of their hillock of brushwood and leaves and flowers, her face took on an expression of ever-increasing joy, and she rushed about like a child at her work.

When the mound had reached their waistlines, Helena sugguested that they light it. The old woman nodded eagerly, and pulled some matches out from under her skirt. She pushed some paper under the branches and lit it. A column of smoke rose slowly, then broke into flame. Madame Neufeld clapped her hands with glee, and walked around the fire. "Come," she said, and took Helena's hand. They walked around the fire together as the flames licked higher and higher. Gradually as they went round and round, Madame Neufeld fell into a sort of dance step, and out of her mouth came a slow chant, "Igo, Igo." Helena fell in with her step. The smoke from the fire swirled about them, and made them toss their heads with closed eyes. Helena joined in the chanting. "Igo, Igo." And as the flames grew higher, their step increased in speed.

Both women felt the same sense of emotional release in the rhythm of the movements. It was as if all the heaviness, the limitations, the weaknesses of their bodies' blood and bone and muscle were melted off them and they had become one with endless, effortless action. It was a strange and dizzying world they had entered into, and there was no more need of reason. The faster they turned and chanted, the nearer they seemed to be to an undefined and rapturous goal. Their hair fell about their faces, gleaming in the mad flames. Their lips trembled with the name, their voices grew hoarse, their bodies bent forward. In their now wide-open unconscious eyes the elements of earth, fire, and water went into a spin.

Suddenly Helena broke the circle and dashed for the water. Madame Neufeld rushed around the fire once before becoming aware of the other's absence. She paused, staggering, her eyes staring about her. She saw the white figure of Helena making for the water, and with a hoarse cry she started after her.

Helena was moving more slowly, as if in a trance. The old woman swept upon her like a black bird, croaking out, "Come back! Come back! For the death of my son you must live and suffer. Come back! Come back!"

The water was about to their knees when she reached Helena, and grabbed her around the waist. In dead silence a peculiar struggle began. They seemed to be swaying, locked in embrace, until one of them stumbled and both collapsed into the icy grip of the river.

It shocked them into consciousness, and brought their minds back to reality. Helena was the first to get up. She caught Madame Neufeld by the arms and dragged her with difficulty to the shore. Together they got up the bank and let their tired, wet bodies sink beside the slowly dying fire. They breathed heavily and made no movement, their faces covered with a glaze of water, their hands heavy as lead.

Farther down river, the human voices were thinning, the fires dying out, the sky growing darker. The wind was rising, chopping up the surface of the Vistula, picking up dry leaves and tossing them into the waters.

"We must keep on living," said the old woman in a whisper. "We must go on living and suffering for Igo."

Helena's head came up slowly, but the expression on her face showed no change. It seemed to her that she could find no difference between life and death. Everything seemed to her the same color, the same odor, and the world had but one aspect.

The bonfire had subsided to a few embers, and the wind was stirring up ashes and scattering sparks which died.

"Come to my house," said Madame Neufeld getting to her feet. "Let's hurry. We cannot let Igo wait for us."

Helena glanced at the old woman, her hands coming up and with stiff fingers brushing back her hair. Her pale face shone in the night, despite the growth of darkness, and the copper of her hair still shone.

"Come on, come on! Igo is waiting," prompted Madame Neufeld, taking her hand and helping her up, as if out of a dream.

Madame Neufeld knew her way around so well, from all her trips to the riverside, that it took them very little time to reach the road to Krzemionki. By side roads and short cuts they reached the old house hidden on its hill of oaks and chestnuts. They even rushed while going up hill, for they could not let Igo wait for them.

As they approached the house, they could see that the lights were lit inside. They hurried up to the windows and looked in. It was bright and warm and inviting inside, and they could hear the sound of two voices, one of a woman and one of a man.

28. ON THE EDGE OF EARTH

BOZENTA CHLAPOWSKI began to feel that in most cases concerning his wife the most simple things were in reality the most complex. By May he was in Paris, where he had several personal affairs to settle. He had also undertaken to confer with the director of the Comédie Française who wanted Helena to perform in the fall of 1903 in the French classic repertoire.

It was apparently quite simple. After her spring appearance in Cracow, Helena would come to Paris, and together they would go for a summer vacation in Switzerland. Helena had promised to keep up a constant correspondence with him, and, most important, she was to let him know the exact time of her arrival in Paris. But things were not working out that way. Bozenta had written her several letters each week, and had received no reply. Two months passed and the spring season in the Cracow theatres ended. There was still no word from Helena.

Bozenta wrote letters to Jozef Kotarbinski, for surely the director would be in close touch with Helena. Kotarbinski replied that he had not seen Helena for several weeks. Bozenta wrote another frantic letter. After all, it was the director who had invited Helena to Cracow in the first place. Kotarbinski promised to search for her and to do his best to convince her to return to her husband. Bozenta threatened to come to Cracow himself. Lucyna was mortified at her husband's negligence. She accused the director of exhausting the actress with his theatre work, and now not even knowing what had become of her.

A search throughout Cracow began. Letters were written, and telegrams, to Lwow and Poznan. It was Lucyna's thought that perhaps the actress had gone there. Perhaps she was a friend's home or at some hotel, soaking in a tub of cold water. She knew that Helena was an enthusiastic follower of the Kneipp system for the cure of nervousness and other neurological complaints. It had come to the point where she would bathe in cold water several times a day, declaring that it helped her health and gave her a crisp and hale appearance.

The Kotarbinskis had been amused by what they regarded as part of their friend's eccentricity. Neither of them knew anything about medicine. They smiled tolerantly when they found that Helena had come back from the United States armed with new names for her ailments. One she described as thrombophlebitis, which affected the heart and the blood vessels. Another pertained to the kidneys, and was called Bright's disease. For these ailments and all others, Helena relied on the Kneipp system—cold baths, cold baths, morning, noon, and night. It had become such a mania with her that no doctor could persuade her that an excess of cold water can be harmful to the human body. Besides, she had no confidence in Polish doctors and was delighted with the American specialist, Dr. J. C. Boyd.

After a vain search in the more obvious places, Lucyna had an inspiration. After all, Helena had told her some of the secrets of her life. She went with her husband to the house of Madame Neufeld at Krzemionki. There they found her, apparently quite contented, but they induced her to come back with them. At the Kotarbinski house, Helena promptly took a cold bath, and rubbed her body down with cold water. She came out declaring herself to be much better. She talked brightly of leaving Cracow the next day. She even asked Kotarbinski to wire her husband to say that she was on her way and to wait for her in Paris.

Lucyna did not leave Helena's side for a moment. Together they did the last-minute shopping. Together they packed Helena's things. So that there would be no further hitches it had been arranged between the Kotarbinskis that they would accompany Helena to Paris. Helena was not yet aware of her friends' intention, but she suspected something from Lucyna's constant presence. Just before departure, when Kotarbinski had already bought three tickets to Paris via Berlin, Helena announced that she was going to Switzerland through Vienna.

"I will go to the Paderewskis' villa in Morges," Helena explained to Lucyna. "It's on the shores of Lake Leman. It will be so beautiful there, and I can really rest. Then from there I will go straight to New York. And what's more I will take Madame Neufeld along with me to America. I like this old lady very much. I can talk with her to my heart's content, about the present and the past. Together we shall plan our trip and our life."

Lucyna was thunderstruck and could find nothing to say. Above all, she did not want to upset Helena. It was during supper. The actress looked radiant and rosy after her cold bath. She wore a white camellia pinned at her waist against her violet gown. The maid was serving dessert of fresh gooseberries. Helena smiled happily. "You know, Lake Leman is as green as Polish gooseberries, a sort of transparent green. Old Madame Neufeld is going to be amazed at the sight of it. Oh, she's going to love Switzerland altogether."

Lucyna was trembling with nervousness. She kept throwing glances at her husband, hoping he would say something. But he merely ate his compote with relish, while Helena continued talking.

"From Switzerland through Italy, or through France, or even through Germany—it will depend on her—we'll go to America. As for the rest of the trip, we'll decide that at Morges. Let the old lady visit some places before her death. She'll know the world better. I have already told her this whole plan of mine, and she has agreed to it. She absolutely wants to live with me in California. And who knows? Maybe when she gets there and feels the warmth of that sun on her and breathes in the scent of the flowers that cover the orange trees, she might live to a hundred and more. Now she's alone in that big house and it makes her despondent. But I like her very much, and will take her away with me. We will go for walks together in the San Iago Canyon. Do you know, that canyon reminds me so much of the Carpathian Mountains. It's a shame when you like the mountain climate so much, Lucyna, that you can't come with us."

"Why not?" Lucyna quickly inserted. She was surprised by her own thought, but something had to be said.

"Yes? That's fine. We'll all go."

Kotarbinski finished his dessert and pushed back his chair. He offered Helena a cigarette, which she took. "Perhaps not to

America," he said slowly. "But we would gladly go with you to Paris."

"We even have tickets," Lucyna added hopefully.

"Tickets? But why?"

Kotarbinski lit her cigarette and his own. He was taking his time. "Your husband particularly asked us to accompany you to Paris."

"Yes, yes," confirmed Lucyna. "I'll show you some letters from him. He simply begged us to come."

Kotarbinski watched Helena's face shrewdly. He saw there the mingled feelings of uneasiness and wonder. He, as director of so famous a theatre as Cracow's, had had a great deal of experience with the leading actors and actresses of Europe. The more talented they were the more difficult they were to handle, he felt. He surmised Helena Modjeska might prove the toughest problem of them all. Without further thought, therefore, he decided to be wholly diplomatic.

"Anything you propose, Helena, we agree to."

"Really? Do you mean that?"

He nodded. Kotarbinski had the reputation of being a ruthless administrator with a hand of iron, a man who expected absolute compliance with his views on how things should run. The greatest of European artists had lost many arguments with him. It was no wonder that Helena stared at him open-mouthed. Lucyna was no less surprised. But he paid no attention, and continued without permitting an interruption.

"We'll all four go to Paris first. You, Madame Neufeld, Lucyna, and I. There we'll meet your husband. From there we'll go to Morges to visit Ignacy Paderewski. When we are there, we can decide how we'll get to New York—by Italian, French, or German boat. Is that what you would like? You tell me."

Helena was radiant. She would like nothing better than to return to her California ranch with friends from Europe. "Why that's wonderful! Wonderful!" she cried. "We can all live very comfortably at my California place. Do you know my place there has two thousand acres. Some people have named it 'The Forest of Arden.' Oh, we'll talk, take walks, enjoy ourselves. We'll talk about our younger days, and the future. I'll have you meet all the leading actors of the American stage.

America is a beautiful land, Jozef. It's full of life and things new. The theatre is alive over there, always ready for advanced ideas. I'm sure I can find you a place in the American theatre. You'll produce plays over there, show them your technique. Part of the year you can live in New York, near your theatre, and part of the year you can come to Arden and spend your vacations with me as my guest."

She laughed happily. She was like a child. How beautiful she was when she was happy! Helen knew everything would be all right if she had with her Igo's mother, Lucyna, and her talented husband. Still more exciting was the thought of playing such a trick on every gossip in Poland. They had tried hard to break up her friendship with Jozef Kotarbinski. Now she would flaunt her friendship in their faces by walking with him right out of Poland. She began to picture their life at Arden. It became a sort of fantasy. It was easy for her to believe in it, as though it had already come about.

"You probably don't realize that Arden and all the fruit orchards with the different buildings and the most modern furniture cost me over a hundred thousand dollars. There's enough room there for hundreds of people. In fact, I've just had a wonderful thought. In traveling through Europe let's stop at all the great cities where there are the best actors and directors and singers of Europe, and let's invite them all to Arden for a free vacation. See, I will cover all the costs. We'll take over to America the most famous artists of Europe together with the poor and unknowns whose talents have not yet been recognized."

It seemed to Helena that Jozef and Lucyna were listening to her plan with great interest. She rushed on with her thoughts.

"The leading artists will be able to help us find the young, talented people in each of the big theatre centers. Of course, I myself am well acquainted with the London and Paris theatres. It will be easy. We'll make it an annual event. Each year several dozen artists will come over to America to live with me. If I need to, I can always build more houses on my ranch. Think what a wonderful effect it will have on American culture. And how it will help culture in Europe, too."

Helena talked on, hardly stopping for breath in her excitement, and smoking one cigarette after another, while her kind hosts listened with an interest that was steadily growing. There was definitely something in this plan of hers. They knew what Helena was like. She did not speak aimlessly when she spoke of spending her own money for the benefit of other artists, and she was always ready to tax her own strength to the danger point in carrying out such a project.

Nevertheless, fate was to play its own part in the proceedings. During their energetic preparations for departure, Madame Neufeld, having approached the eightieth year of her life, fell into a deep sleep and never awoke. The Kotarbinskis went to Paris with Helena as they had promised. But here the fantasy came to an abrupt end. Kotarbinski could not bring himself to quit a most excellent position in one of the best theatres in Europe. He could not be expected to start over in a new country at his age. Perhaps it was right that he had not the courage. Helena listened to his excuses with understanding and sympathy.

But Helena was hardly interested any more. A new wave of melancholy had taken hold of her, and left her indifferent to matters great or small. She and Bozenta saw the Kotarbinskis off on the train back to Cracow. A few days later, the Chlapowskis were on their way to the United States. All thought of Switzerland had been abandoned.

Instead of expensive Paris gowns and costumes, Helena's bags were filled with marsh marigolds and other flowers from the moors and meadows of her homeland, together with bottles of water taken from the river Vistula.

29. ADIEU LA GRANDE ARTISTE

HELENA HAD in her possession a photograph of Ignacy Paderewski, on which he had written: "To a loving Helena with a plea for fond remembrance." Years ago, in Poland, she had helped the pianist at the start of his career. In those early days she had been enchanted by his playing, and did all she could to make his first concert a success. Afterwards, when he needed to go to Vienna for further study, she made all the arrangements for the trip. Her faith in him was well rewarded. The critics agreed that this Paderewski could play Chopin as nobody had yet done. He was hailed as a composer as well as a pianist, and climbed steadily to a position of world renown.

As for Paderewski, he always wished he could find some way to show his gratitude to Helena. On coming to American shores he thought he saw his opportunity. He approached the theatrical producer Daniel Frohman with an idea. Frohman had known Helena for some time. In fact, she had been under his management at one period. He agreed to go with the pianist to California in the hope that they could stir Modjeska out of her useless retirement at San Iago Canyon, persuade her to rid herself of the cares and expense of ranch life, and sign up with Frohman for an extended tour through America and Canada. The two friends arrived full of optimism at Arden in January of 1905.

Helena Modjeska was now almost sixty-five, but her appearance gave no indication that she was well on in years. She looked as young and healthy and vibrant as a woman of less than half her age. She was capable of sudden bursts of activity when she sparkled with laughter and playful fun, displaying a depth of joy that affected everyone around her. But Paderewski did not know the other side, the dark moods that were closely related to her physical illnesses. At such times she would fall into brooding melancholy that would last for several hours,

235

sometimes for days, for weeks, or even months. And the whole atmosphere around her would be thrown into misery. Bozenta was the one to suffer more than the others. The business of running an immense ranch was a task far beyond his strength. These black fits of his wife plunged him into anguish.

Helena would lapse into a condition that was like a dream. She apparently had no desire to dress herself or to eat her meals. She would only talk of her past, the days of her youth, and repeatedly cried out that her life had been ruined. She would retire into her room, surrounded with old paintings, books, inscribed Greek vases, and other fascinating and fantastic antiques that she had steadily collected from all over the world, and she would act out her classic roles. She would hold long conversations, or rather monologues, with Shakespeare, Molière, Schiller, and other great dramatists, as though they were in the room with her. Afterwards, she would fall into a sleep so deep that she could not be roused. She would wake up then full of energy, with a general brilliance of mind, but complaining of pains in her chest, her heart, and kidneys.

The mysterious fact was that these ailments at other times seemed to be nonexistent for her, as she went about her activities around the house. She organized picnic trips with her son who would often come to visit her, and studied and improved her Shakespearean parts. Lately, she had begun to study Hermann Sudermann's *Magda*. As she said, "I found in the title part one of my favorite and most successful roles. I was attracted not so much by the Bohemianism, the plea for woman's rights, as by Magda's enthusiasm for art, and her awareness of the high mission of an artist."

In her talks with her two friends, Helena showed all her enthusiasm over the prospect of doing *Magda* some time on the stage, and they in their turn used this great opportunity in their arguments. Accept the contract that Frohman was suggesting to her and she would be able to put on the play without delay, besides giving to the world again her brilliant performance in *Macbeth, Antony and Cleopatra, The Merchant of Venice, Henry VIII, As You Like It, Camille, Marie Stuart, Marie Antoinette,* and whatever else she wished. Paderewski spoke of her great acting talent as a gift from heaven that must not be kept

in hiding, but must be set up for all to see, to become a light to
the struggling heart of humanity and an inspiration to the
young, the students, the artists of the new generation. She had
helped him once when he most needed encouragement. The philosophy was hers. She should now use it on herself.

Helena promised she would think about the proposition. She
decided her friends were right about her selling the ranch. It
was a drain on her strength, and more important a drain on
her finances. She would find somewhere to live without ex-
cessive costs, without servants perhaps. She would probably
retire to her small house on Bay Island in East Newport, California, where only eighteen families lived on the entire island.
She had money enough in the bank to keep her comfortable for
the rest of her life, besides close to two hundred thousand dollars' worth of jewelry and antiques, but some inexplicable need
within her at this time made her suddenly tighten up on all ex-
penditures.

She put her ranch up for sale and immediately went into a fit
of despondency over it. What would she do with all her things,
since she didn't want to part with anything, and there was no
room for them at Bay Island. She still retained a romantic
sentiment about Arden and its glorious isolation, being ten miles
from the nearest railroad and twenty-three miles from Santa
Ana. The ranch house itself, called a "bungalow type," had been
designed especially for her by her friend and admirer, the architect Stanford White. As for the canyon with its torrent of
waters, it reminded her pleasantly of some parts of the Carpathian Mountains. She had spent much time there in the company of her friends. There were also places in the canyon that
had a special meaning for her and for her alone, for she told no
one, not even her husband, of her secret walks into the canyon
after the fiery setting of the sun, where she would relive her
past years and remember the happiness of her passionate youth.

Bozenta, for his part, was not satisfied with the mere selling
of the ranch. He liked to look ahead to some prospects for the
future. He was accustomed to living like the aristocrat that
he was. There was plenty of use for her money. He was a good
businessman and he would control it. When he learned from
Daniel Frohman that he and Jules Murry wanted to organize

a tour for his wife, he was enthusiastic and at once commenced new plans of his own.

There were two major problems facing Bozenta. The first was the uncertainty of Helena's intentions. Somehow she must be convinced that her friend Paderewski was right, that she owed it to the world to make one more series of appearances before absolute retirement. The second problem was to arrange the tour with Jules Murry in such a way that there would be enough time between appearances for her to recover from her periods of ill health. The real state of her health must be kept an absolute secret. It was necessary therefore to work quickly and carefully. To begin with, there was to be an elaborate celebration in her honor in New York. Apart from the publicity involved, it would serve to convince Helena that the public was clamoring to see her on the stage again. The most distinguished personages of the artistic world should come to this event to pay her homage. With the sound of their praises in her ears, she would begin her tour with renewed confidence, and, so Bozenta hoped, strength.

In April, 1905, a letter arrived from Daniel Frohman, together with a collective letter signed by the great figures of art —writers, composers, painters and actors:

To Madame Helena Modjeska:

The undersigned, your friends and admirers, with many others whose names do not appear here, desire to tender you a public testimonial in recognition of your services to the stage, and as an expression of our appreciation of your genius and our regard for your character, we feel, dear Madame, that all that we can do must be an inadequate attempt to discharge the great debt we owe you. In you, the art of acting in our day has rejoiced in one of the loftiest exponents. Shakespeare has found in you an interpreter worthy of his most exquisite and thrilling imagination, and in the range of modern tragedy and comedy the refinement and charm of your every impersonation have ennobled the original.

If agreeable to you, the performance, in which we hope for your personal cooperation, will take place at the Metropolitan Opera House on May 2.

Helena was overjoyed, and with new heart she traveled to New York a few days before the designated date. She wanted to talk to Paderewski, whom she suspected of having more than a little to do with the organization of this great event, but her dear Ignacy had been injured while traveling, and was confined to bed, unable to see her or to take any active part in the gala May afternoon festivities. But he managed to write a letter, which was read from the stage of the old Metropolitan Opera House:

For many months I have been looking forward to the 2nd of May, anticipating one of the greatest joys of my career. The thought of joining you all on this solemn occasion has been my pride for many months. The sudden adversity of fate makes me feel now grieved and humiliated, and words cannot express all the bitterness of my disappointment. But there is still a pride and joy I cannot be deprived of—the pride of belonging to the same country, to the same race which sent into the wide world one of the greatest and noblest artists of all times and nations; the joy of being one of many to whom Madame Modjeska had been good, kind, and generous. The first encouraging words I heard as a pianist came from her lips; the first successful concert I had in my life was due to her assistance. Unable to be present, I beg of you to convey to Madame Modjeska the homage of my profound admiration and gratitude, and to extend my sincerest thanks to all who contribute to make this day the day of legitimate and crowning triumph for a career great, noble, pure, and beautiful.

The great auditorium was filled with guests from all over the world, filled to overflowing. More than a thousand people stood outside because of the lack of space. Inside was a picture of splendor and radiance. The great and near-great contributed to making this one of the most memorable occasions and most fitting tributes to a genius of the stage. Prominent actresses sold programs, candy, and souvenirs of all kinds in the lobby, amassing a small fortune for the swelling fund. The program, which was handsomely printed on heavy plate paper, contained portraits in halftone of all the artists participating in the affair.

Jeannette L. Gilder, writer and critic, wrote a special critical appreciation of Modjeska for the program, while her brother, Richard Watson Gilder, editor of *The Century* composed a commendatory poem:

There are four sisters, known to mortals well,
Whose names are Joy and Sorrow, Death, and Love.
This last it was who did my footsteps move
To where the other deep-eyed sisters dwell.
Tonight, or ere yon painted curtain fell,
These, one by one, before my eyes did rove
Through the brave mimic world that Shakespeare wove.
Lady! thy art, thy passion were the spell
·That held me, and still holds; for thou dost show,
With those most high, each in his sovereign art—
Shakespeare supreme, and mighty Angelo—
Great art and passion are one! Thine, too, the part
To prove that still for him the laurels grow
Who reaches through the mind to pluck the heart!

Among the many famous actors and actresses taking part in
the great proceedings were Ada Rehan, Mrs. Patrick Campbell,
Mary Shaw, Louis James, John Kellard, Joseph Haworth,
James O'Neill, and David Bisphan. Helena was so moved by
the sincere expression of so much love and admiration from so
many, that she performed a scene from *Macbeth* with such mas-
tery that the audience was held spellbound. She took her applause in a magnificent tableau, the participating actors standing around her—on either side of her, elegantly dressed pages
holding flaming torches on high, Modjeska in the center robed
in white save for an orange scarf draped about her shoulders.

As the actress stepped forward, Edmund Clarence Stedman
walked across the stage to present her with an illuminated
memorial hung with the symbols of her native and adopted
lands, the American and Polish national colors, and in ringing
accents he addressed her:

"Madame Modjeska, it is my grateful office to present you
with the address in response to which you make this day so
memorable. The scroll bears the signatures of brothers and sisters of your own profession, and of your attached votaries in
other walks of life—all united in devotion to the drama and
to the cognate arts of beauty and expression, and all made now
associates by their delight in your genius and career. So absolute is the sincerity of their homage, so manifest at this moment

the gift and personality which have inspired it, that I might well
end here with the lines of an old English poet:

> Enough! and leave the rest to Fame!
> 'Tis to commend her, but to name.

Yet, for our own honor and content, we would fain, like Viola,
go on with our 'speech in your praise, and then show you the
heart' of a tribute worth even more to the givers than to her
who receives it."

Stedman went on to speak of her valorous country, "that
martyr-land, alas, bleeding this hour for Freedom," the land
of Pulaski and Kosciuszko, of Chopin, Sembrich and Paderewski, and of Modjeska. He spoke of her great playing of
Shakespearean roles that "awoke in us the sense of 'something
rich and strange.'" He recalled that other great testimonial
when she played Ophelia with "the princely Booth" as a tribute
to Lester Wallack. He named the great names that assisted her
that day, and concluded: "That radiant hemicycle has vanished!
Last of all, Jefferson has returned to the mountain, and we shall
see his smile no more. You, their younger sister, to whom they
gave their pride and support—long may your enviable years
flow on, consecrated alike by the starlight of the past and the
sunshine of the present!"

Helena accepted the memorial with tears in her eyes. But she
replied with an unusual speech, for she began by talking not of
herself but of another actress, nineteen years her junior, whom
she designated as the greatest living actress of the day:

". . . Eleonora Duse came to America as the exponent of the
newest dramatic methods of the so-called 'realistic' school of
acting. Generally speaking, I do not take great interest in all this
talk about the different schools of acting. It seems to me that
there are only two schools, one of good acting, the other of bad
acting. Thus in the case of Madame Duse, I cared much less for
her particular modernistic methods than for her own self and
her artistic powers. Whatever school she belongs to, she is a
great actress."

Here all the audience imagined that she was unconsciously
thinking of herself, even while she spoke of Duse, who had

made her debut in America twelve years before, and had thrilled
the critics with a style of acting that was so different from that
of the flamboyant Bernhardt. But the great Modjeska continued: "The intensity with which she abandons herself to the
feelings of the character she impersonates makes you forget all
surroundings, you do not realize any more that you are at the
theatre, that there is an actress on the boards; you cease anal-
yzing, you only feel that you are in the presence of terrible pain,
despair, and agony."

Helena's face had become deathly pale. She stopped, and as
if with her last remaining ounce of strength, she ended: "I shall
never forget her wonderful last act in Dumas' *Camille,* nor the
thrill that passed through me, at the very end of *Fedore,* by a
single phrase, '*E la Morte,*' when she drinks the poisoned cup."

She paused. There was an immediate wave of applause
through the house. Then she continued, and it was clear that she
had regained control over her emotions. She began to speak of
a subject that had interested her through her entire career:

"It has been often mentioned, both in England and America,
that in order to render faithfully Shakespeare's creations, one
must be of English stock, on the plea that the poet was himself
an Englishman, and therefore could only bring forth personages
endowed with English characteristics, which cannot be success-
fully grasped by foreigners. This argument seems both narrow
and disparaging to the genius of Shakespeare. We foreigners,
born outside of the Anglo-Saxon race, place Shakespeare upon
a much higher pedestal. We claim that, before being English,
he was human, and that his creations are not bound either by
local or ethnological limits, but belong to humanity in general.
One might as well say that Shakespeare could only be rightly
comprehended and interpreted by his contemporaries, for certainly the English people of the Elizabethan era were very different from their descendants of the twentieth century. If our
poet was not able to reproduce truthfully Italians, Moors, or
Spaniards, he certainly could not be well acquainted with the
idiosyncrasies of these who were to be born a hundred years
after his time. And yet, are the sentiments and passions which
animate the characters of his plays so different from those of
our generation? Our argument is that when Shakespeare wanted

to present English people he located them in England, or at least gave them English names, Sir Toby Belch, Sir Andrew Aguecheek, etc., while when he presents Romans, Greeks, Jews, Italians, or Moors, he does not mean them to be travesties of Anglo-Saxons, but to have the characteristics of their own nations and race. It is evident to me that it was not without purpose that he made Othello a Moor, Romeo and Juliet Italians, and Coriolanus a Roman patrician. It is a southern sun that warms the atmosphere of the romance of Verona: it is the fire of African blood that runs through the veins of Desdemona's lover; it is the cruelty inborn to his race that prompts him to murder her; and it is the pride of the conquerors of the world which swells the bosom of Coriolanus. The feelings and compassions typified in Shakespeare's plays animated all humanity, and this is the reason why the Bard of Avon is equally understood, admired, and loved all the world over and, *grany przeze mnie tez* (and played also by me)."

And now as if she could no longer endure it, she started finally to speak in earnest about herself, her own life's work:

"When I was young I yearned for fame, but later on, all other considerations paled against the enthusiasm of the work itself. I fell in love with my art. To get out of myself, to forget all about Helena Modjeska, to throw my whole soul into the assumed character, to lead its life, to be moved by its emotions, thrilled by its passions, to suffer or rejoice—in one word, to identify myself with it and reincarnate another soul and body— this became my ideal, the goal of all my aspirations, and at the same time the enchantment and attraction of my work. Friends who are familiar with my work claim that I have some right to say a few words about dramatic art. 'Is it an art, indeed?' asked once a skeptical acquaintance of mine, who had seen a comic-opera singer, a person he knew to be without any training, with no artistic instincts, and of a very commonplace turn of mind, achieve a success in a serious drama. I was myself puzzled, but I watched carefully the performer, and discovered that the acting, though effective, was purely mechanical. When I think of this incident, I cannot help observing that the correct interpretation of a part is not always *ipso facto* a work of art. Something else is needed, something which ought to lie in the very depth of the actor's soul, the suggestion of which has much more value than even the most laborious study . . . it seems to me to be an irrepressible desire of expression, together with the riches of feeling, which one can open to the world. Those who are endowed with this sense of expression, and moreover can enhance it with the color of their imagination and the intensity of emotional temperament, achieve what a mechanical though excellent performer can never do. They thrill the audience, which will carry home some of the actor's inmost treasures and live on them for a while. The richer his nature, the better the influence.

"'The more I give, the more I have,' says Juliet. To give and give is our task. This does not mean that actors get nothing from the outside world. On the contrary, a keen sense of observation will help them to store their minds and give back to people the very thing they got from them in a different form. Some of the actors possess a gift of close observation and analysis which might be envied by many psychologists. But in personating dramatic or tragic parts one cannot depend solely on the documents furnished even by the closest observation. While tragic situations produced by them are usually concealed and hidden before outsiders, the ludicrous features of men, on the contrary, are most often exposed to our view. It is therefore in his own soul and in his imagination, it is to his own power of expression that he must trust to reproduce the reality of the feeling. The actor who is not impressionable, who is not stirred within himself, has to rely on elocution and conventional methods. But his work will be cold and mechanical in spite of his assiduous and meritorious efforts. All theatrical devices, all the display of lung power, will not give life to a dead-born personation. The artist who feels makes the public feel.

"The ideal actor, it seems to me, must possess intelligence, quick perception, originality, impressionability, and imagination enough to allow him to identify himself with an assumed character, and above all, a store of emotion and passion. Besides those, he has to possess many physical attributes, as, for instance, an expressive face, a . . . ."

Here her voice broke off. She took up a glass of water from the table and drank some of it. The color seemed to drain from her face again as she looked up and began to speak again. But it appeared that she had forgotten her former train of thought and was starting on something else. There was a moment's stirring and a wave of murmuring swept through the audience.

"The dramatic schools in America," Helena continued, "such as they are—and a few of them are very good, indeed—are very expensive, and only those who can afford to pay the required sum can receive tuition and a subsequent engagement. Such a system presents two drawbacks: First, young people who have talent and no money are deprived of the advantages the school could give them. Second, those schools being planned on a business basis, every one who pays is admitted. The result is that they produce aspirants for the dramatic career without the slightest qualification for it, who only increase the number of bad actors and actresses. Therefore, I welcome with joy the advent of the National Theatre in New York, which will, like the Théâtre Français, have in connection with it a dramatic school, where only students who give indication of talent will be accepted, and where the tuition and training will be offered without pay. I am very fortunate indeed that I was present at the birth of this idea and was able to add my helping hand to the work involved in inaugurating this very important institution in this young and dynamic and up-coming country. The establishment of the National Theatre will undoubtedly have a beneficent influence on the development of the dramatic art in the United States."

She bowed, and turned as if to walk off the stage. But the thunderous applause which greeted her held her back. The audience gave her a standing ovation, and cheered her until they were hoarse. Helena bowed once more, walked with faltering step off stage, and the curtain came down.

It was to be her last appearance in New York, the city where she had really begun her American career over a quarter of a century before. Nevertheless, all felt her playing of the *Macbeth* scene, together with her speech, was the most intensely dramatic performance she had yet given. Helena, herself, came away with a great feeling of elation. She knew now how much she was loved. The renewed persuasion of Paderewski, Frohman, and Jules Murry proved irresistible. Her only fear, a fear

which she kept to herself, was that she would some time break
down while on the stage.

Her tour proved such a fantastic triumph that it was extended into April of 1907. Helena received an ovation wherever
she went, but her health grew steadily worse. Performances had
to be so spaced and arranged that there would be ample time for
travel and rest between appearances. Her repertoire was not
new. She was repeating for the last times her unforgettable
creations of Shakespeare's plays, but with a new, incredible fury
of youthful passion. The audiences detected the difference and
watched astonished, then hypnotized, as they came under her
spell. It was as if there was some intangible power controlling
her every action, forcing a superhuman greatness out of her.
She was no longer an actress approaching the age of retirement,
but some mysterious vehicle of dynamic emotion. The tragic
implications of her acting overwhelmed her audiences and sent
them into ecstasies, but as a residue there was inevitably present
a fearful awareness that something unusual was taking place in
the actress, both on stage and off. There began to be that double
reaction to her performances, made up of admiration and alarm,
a sense that she was giving too much for human endurance, that
perhaps the next minute something would happen on the stage.

Yet she continued playing—her voice, with its incredible
range, her large, deep eyes casting their spell.

30. THIS SIDE OF FATE

THE LAST scenes of the drama were drawing to their end behind the white doors of a lonely iron-fenced house on Bay Island.

There was a depressingly barren look about this island, its rolling hillsides of sand, its eighteen silent houses that baked in the fierce California sun. The ocean heaved, and the wind came in fits like hot breath. The iron fence stood off a tangle of rambling roses that dropped in the heat and wept browning petals that, drop by drop, struck the ground like stones. Even the deep barking of Wicek, the noisiest of the dogs, whose main profession was to chase away the cats, had long gasped himself to an absent silence. There was no trace of cats' paws on the sandy waterless soil. The stubbornnest of the birds had given up hope of crumbs and escaped the morbid silence to seek out a friendlier house. The sun's intensity, so unbearable to plant and beast, was blistering the dark paint on the house walls and the white window frames. But the close secrets within were safeguarded by the drawn curtains.

Charles Bozenta Chlapowski, a grayed, bent, and stumbling figure, moved slowly among boxes, chests, and packages, as he carried article of every description from the adjacent rooms into the living room. He packed each object delicately away, frequently shaking his head and blinking his eyes, raising his eyebrows and squinting. Whenever he found himself at all close to the securely bolted doors leading to the library, or, as he called it, "the wife's studio," he would step away with startling alacrity, muttering to himself in Latin *"Memento mori quia pulvis es et pulveri reverteris. . . .* (Remember, that dust you are and to dust you will return)." Then with renewed energy he would turn to further packing, as if his one desire was to leave this house, this island, indeed the entire country, as soon as possible.

Nothing interested Bozenta any more, not his aristocratic

247

titles, nor the money he had so desired in times past, nor love
for anyone or anything. He felt that his life had become sati-
ated. His one need was to be able to breathe freely again. Here,
in this house, it was quite impossible. If he remained, he would
become suffocated by the depressive atmosphere. He would
shrivel up in the burning heat. His tired face only broke into
a smile when he discovered standing out, as in relief against
the hazy images in his mind, the picture of the green fields and
meadows of his estates in Cracow and Poznan. These fleeting
mind pictures, stirred with such refreshing, cool breezes on wet,
green growing things, came and went like mirages in a desert.
But it was his driving fixation to reach the reality of them.
Nothing else concerned him, whether his wife died today or
tomorrow, whether he was left in poverty or in wealth. He must
return to the place of his birth, for in his troubled mind it had
become a sort of shrine of miraculous power that would rid
him of the heaviest affliction and return to him his manhood.

His body was clamped in a constant embrace of weariness.
His eyelids drooped incessantly so that it became a matter of
huge willpower to see what he was doing. He had been on his
feet for over a month from the earliest morning hours to the
latest hours at night. By the middle of the day he became so
exhausted that he was all but falling asleep while walking. Yet
still he had to pack the silverware, and those oil paintings he
had purchased with his wife's money on their trips across
Europe.

He gazed around the room. Piles of books and clothes lay
among the boxes, waiting for hands to put them in a free and
safe place, but he no longer had the strength. He subsided into
an armchair and immediately his head fell forward. He dozed
off. Now and then he jerked his head awake and half started,
only to slip back into slumber. In his moments of half consciousness he knew he had to take advantage of every moment that
his wife left him in peace, for as soon as she knocked on the
door, it meant she wanted water, or some Shakespearean book,
or a bouquet of the withering roses from the garden. Whatever
it was, he had to answer her bidding at once. It made no difference what time of the day or night it was, for if he was not
quick enough she would fall into a fit of rage and would curse

him with such violence that he would feel quite defenseless and physically weak. If he was prompt in returning with what she wanted, she would give him a commendatory smile, before she would cry out, as if suddenly struck by fear of time's headlong rush, "I want to be alone! I want to be alone! I want to be alone!" And her door would be locked again.

Since she had already discharged all the servants, he was compelled to wait on her without any outside aid. In the matter of meals there was no trouble, for she ate absolutely nothing beyond fruits—oranges, grapes, and apples. All he had to do was bring her several buckets of water each day, which she would snatch out of his grasp eagerly, as if water were the most precious substance in the world. And so it had gone on for more than a month. That is, since Frank Fowler had finished his assignment and left her library for the last time.

Helena had known the artist, Fowler, for many years. Their friendship had started at the time of his first exhibition at the Society of American Artists in New York, where he displayed his portraits of America's most beautiful women. Many years before, the French painter Jules Bastien-Lepage had painted Modjeska. Bastien-Lepage, until his death in 1884, was in great demand in the highest circles of both Europe and America. The actress had ordered her portrait done by him, principally to go along with the style then in vogue, but in the end she regretted it. She was not pleased with his concept of her. There was, besides, insufficient flattery in his picture, too little spirit of warmth. Helena then turned to Frank Fowler, whose fame had been steadily increasing, and whose work had gained more depth. He finished a portrait of Helena in the same year as the death of the Frenchman. Her admiration for Fowler's work remained unchanged, and it came to her mind at last to have him come to Bay Island, so that he could paint the walls of her library with the scenes of her youth and of her successes in Shakespearean roles.

From then on, every day she would lock herself in the enormous library with the artist, telling him of Cracow, of the Vistula, of the Sobotkas of St. John's Eve, of Igo, of her appearances on the European stage, of her tours in America, her successes and her failures. He listened to her with great patience, for she was paying him well for this work, and he painted the four walls from top to bottom with his large brushes which he had brought with all his equipment from Los Angeles.

The entire life of Modjeska became locked in these painted scenes. They started when she was eight years old and had appeared for the first time on any stage in *The Daughter of the Regiment,* for which, not knowing why, she had dressed herself in the traditional costume of the Cracow area, high laced boots, a white pleated skirt, a red bodice embroidered with gold and silver, and on her head a wreath of roses with a mass of long multicolored ribbons cascading over her shoulders.

In telling the artist about this scene she snatched up the various pieces of peasant garb from the piles of costumes strewn haphazardly about the room, and quite unabashed by his presence swiftly transformed herself into the young peasant girl down to the smallest detail. From this, at a nod from Fowler that he had taken in her appearance, she put on the costume of the butterfly in the ballet *The Siren of Dniestr.* Following this, came a scene from Schiller's *Kabale und Liebe,* the role of the Countess in *The White Camellia,* the Italian peasant girl in *The Prima-Donna,* and again Schiller's *The Robbers,* and Sheridan's *School for Scandal.* From these she changed to the costumes of Mary Stuart, Ophelia, Doña Sol from Hugo's *Hernani,* the Wife in *Nos Intimes* by Sardou, and *Adrienne Lecouvreur* of Scribe and Legouvé.

The artist marveled at how quickly she could throw herself into a scene for him, change costumes, talk, sing, scream, cry, wring her hands, and day after day repeat the same actions, going deeper and deeper into her play for the sake of his brush. Perspiration covered her brow, the costumes would cling damply to her body, but she would go on without apparent fatigue. She seemed sustained by an inspiration that would not let her falter. She played Juliet, and then sprang to Lady Anne from *King Richard III,* Titania from *A Midsummer Night's Dream,* Desdemona from *Othello.* Without realizing it she repeated Ophelia, then went on to Rosalind, Beatrice, Viola, Portia—on and on until she lost all sense of continuity. She mixed costumes, scenes, epochs, dialogues, sentences, words, and stopped suddenly, exhausted and trembling.

She turned, dashed to a large basin of cold water standing on a side table, bathed her face, and with the same swift movements returned to the couch. Falling back into it, she cried out in the words of the Countess Idalia: "I am here as a passing angel. I have let thee see the lightning and disappeared upon the firmament of the sky."

A sudden silence ensued. Only her labored breathing was discernible against the sound of the rustling brushes over the wall. Frank Fowler, himself lost in this great play-acting, painted his scenes rapidly as he remembered them. He showed his understanding when Helena threw out her extravagant plea: "If I could only appear youthful. Just as that girl in the Festival of St. John's Eve. Don't change a thing. Let every scene from every play have that same youthful face, and let every hero have the face of Igo. Put in a great deal of water, blue skies, flowers, and above all luck, good fortune. Lock all that up on the walls. I want to live once again, to be forever full of life and enchantment. Nowhere there do I want to see my old body, my aging face. Understand, understand? Remember!"

Fowler nodded his head in solemn agreement and painted like one possessed for hours on end, day after day, in order to finish in the shortest possible time. As he worked he suffered with her, or rather for her, as he had become fully cognizant of the internal torture and mental anguish of her battle with the past, which followed her wherever she went, at every step she took, in every moment of her life. He began to feel that his own existence depended on finishing his work with the utmost speed, for soon he himself would lapse into some morbid state of dreaming, become inextricably tangled in these scenes and fragments from the mind of Shakespeare and Modjeska's remembered life. As it was, he found himself incredibly moved at each successive meeting by her constant appeals to him, that came not alone from the artist in her, but from her as a human being . . . as a woman. Her all-absorbing sincerity made him suffer. He felt it as an anguish. He felt how she longed to be at peace with herself, to be on good terms with the living and the dead, with things animate and inanimate. Yes, he was drawn to her, held by the artistry of her body's motion and expressiveness, and by the poetry of her mind, which often seemed to make no distinction between material existence and the life of her dreams and wishes. For Helena, the people of the past, even of past centuries, and those of the present stood for one soul, a mass of souls in one. It seemed to her she communed with them all, and smiled at all, for each had the same pale and dreaming face, the face of Igo Neufeld.

She now awake from her lethargy. She raised her head and stared at Fowler with mysterious eyes. She put her hand to her hair that was like tarnished copper, and with an absent gesture she stroked it back as if it had been a shadow over her mind. "You know?" she began.

Fowler turned to her, "What?"

"Why do I tell you about Igo? You know already. You look so much like him. Those same dark eyes."

Helena moved quite close to him. Then, taking her trailing gown in both hands, she spread it wide and with a beautifully sweeping motion she went down on one knee before him. She took his hand and kissed it gently.

Then she got up and returned to the couch. There were tears in her eyes as she sat down, her head in her hands, her elbows on her knees. She gazed forlornly at the arabesque designs on the carpet which covered the entire floor. Fowler was reminded of the utterance of William Winter a short while back in the *New York Tribune:* "To mention her name, as the years drift away, will be to recall a presence of stately dignity, of tender poetic beauty, of exquisite refinement, and of perfect grace. . . ."

Glancing at her long fingers, at her smooth forehead, at her massive ringlets of copper hair, he imagined that he had before him some spirit of nature, that could not be robbed of beauty. The light from the silver candlesticks, playing with flattering highlights on her face, gave life and youth to her looks. He turned hastily to his work, lest the image of endless youth escape him.

The walls were swiftly covered with true scenes from the plays of Shakespeare, alongside the scenes of Helena's youth in the costume of Cracow province, full of churches and other noble structures of an ancient past. Meadows blossomed with a riot of yellow flowers, reeds and bushes and weeping willow. Edged by its golden sand, the blue river flowed through. And from every side and from every angle gazed the sparkling eyes of the same girl and the jealous eyes of Igo. The studio gained space and came to life with rhythm and color. The atmosphere of the room itself with its exotic mixture of smells—burning candles, paint, costumes, and flowers—helped the artist to maintain his mood without effort. His brush sped across the walls as if in some trance, and soon he could see that there would not be enough space on the four of them to take all the ideas that burned in his brain.

It was already late when the painter finished. Helena Modjeska had drifted into a state of unconsciousness that seemed to be an exhausted sleep. By the light of the candles that were almost gutted in their own grease, Frank Fowler crossed the room to the door and stepped out on tiptoe. On the outside, the somber countenance of Bozenta greeted him. He was finally escorted to the front door and down the path to the gate that was carefully unlocked for him.

Returning to the house, Bozenta changed his expression of weariness, and muttered, *"Memento mori quia pulvis es et pulveri reverteris."* Again the monotony of silence descended over all like death.

It was at dawn on the 8th of April, 1909, that Helena Modjeska passed away at her home on Bay Island, Orange County, California. Dr. J. C. Boyd wrote out the death certificate very exactly. He set down the cause of death as Bright's disease in addition to prolonged complications of the heart. Her body was transported to Los Angeles and placed in a vault to await transportation back to Poland.

On the 17th of July, Helena Modjeska was buried in the old Cracow cemetery, among the graves of those who had labored for the people of Poland. At the open grave an oration was delivered in rolling tones by her last student, the Shakespearean actor, Michal Tarasiewicz:

You, who have returned to the land that is to be your final place of rest, hail . . . and be blessed for your generous and gentle heart, for your kindness to others, your comeliness and grace. . . . You have departed from us, though like a radiant dream preserved forever in the minds of those who were enchanted by your art. . . .

Let the great city of Cracow receive you in its cemetery, where so many brave hearts have been laid to rest, where the great Jan Matejko lies. . . .

Queen of the dramatic arts, illustrious queen, rest in peace, after your labor, your trials, and your triumphs. . . . May the wind's breath in the weeping willows come to you in tones as sweet as the divine poetry of the stage to comfort your soul in rest, and in return let your genius be the guardian of the Polish stage, upholding that state of glory you have created for it. . . . And may all artists who come here in homage to your grave receive, as at the spring of Castal, faith, vitality, and inspiration, so that great and grateful hearts of future generations will dwell with you in that eternal pantheon of the arts.